Health and Wellbeing

SPHE 2

Anne Potts

Nodlaig O'Grady

The Educational Company of Ireland   Edco

The paper used in this book comes from Managed Forests in Northern Europe. For every tree felled, at least one new tree is planted

First published 2018
The Educational Company of Ireland
Ballymount Road
Walkinstown
Dublin 12

www.edco.ie

A member of the Smurfit Kappa Group plc

ISBN: 978-1-84536-773-2

Book design: Design Image
Cover design: Graftrónaic
Layout: Graftrónaic
Editor: Aoife Barrett (Arcadia Publishing Services)
Editorial Assistant: Michael Kemp
Proofreader: Jane Rogers
Photographs: alamy.com, iStock.com; Shutterstock.com.
Illustrations: Simon Smith (Beehive Illustration); Irish Water Safety; Igloo Animations; iStock.com; Shutterstock.com.

Contents

Introduction

Welcome to *Health and Wellbeing: SPHE 2*. We hope you enjoyed everything you learned and the skills you developed through following this programme last year and are ready to start on year two. This three-year programme is designed to help you to become (or remain!) a confident, happy, healthy and connected young person.

The aims of the health and wellbeing Social Personal and Health Education (SPHE) classes are to give you the space to:

- Learn about yourself
- Care for yourself and others
- Make informed decisions about your health and wellbeing.

Health and Wellbeing: SPHE 2 is designed to involve you in your own learning, by using theory and activities which make you think about the topics, discuss these issues and apply what you have learned to your own life. You will also find follow-up references listed: websites, videos and help agencies. This textbook is full of interesting information and activities which make learning stimulating, such as drama, collage, quizzes, animations, debates, film making, newspaper articles, cartoons, and PowerPoint and oral presentations.

To ensure that you get the most out of SPHE, at the beginning of each unit you will find the **Learning Outcomes** for that unit, which you can tick off as you achieve them. There is also a list of **Key Words** which are explained in clear, simple terms throughout the text, **Did You Know?** boxes with interesting facts, and research findings and background information on each topic.

To help you to keep track of your learning there are **Learning Logs**, **Assessment – Check your Learning** activities and **Unit Reviews**. Work you have completed can be stored in an SPHE folder or electronically in an e-folder. Your oral literacy is developed using debates, class presentations and small group and class discussions, while your digital literacy is helped by producing videos, making slide presentations and taking online quizzes and tests. The use of charts, graphs, surveys, percentages and ratios helps to improve your numeracy skills.

We hope that you continue to enjoy and benefit from your time in post-primary school and that *Health and Wellbeing: SPHE 2* helps you to achieve this!

Anne & Nodlaig

Digital Resources

The *Health and Wellbeing: SPHE 2* digital resources will enhance classroom learning by encouraging student participation and engagement. To aid lesson planning, PowerPoints and animations are **referenced in the textbook** using the following icons:

PowerPoints – cover a range of key topics, including goals and motivation, study skills and mental health

Animations – pose scenarios for students to discuss in class.

Visit **www.edcolearning.ie** to access the *Health and Wellbeing: SPHE 2* e-book and digital resources, which also include **worksheets** to accompany the animations and **weblinks** for each unit. Plus, **exclusive additional resources and information** are available at **ie.reachout.com/edco**, in partnership with **Reachout.com**.

UNIT 1 Self-Management 1 – Making a New Start

Learning Outcomes:

This unit helps you to:

1. Review your first year in post-primary school ⭕
2. Offer some advice to new first years, on how they can make the best of the year ahead ⭕
3. Make a good start to second year ⭕
4. Draw up a set of ground rules for working together in SPHE class. ⭕

(Tick off as you complete them.)

KEY WORDS

Advice

Resolution

Class ground rules

Looking Back, Looking Forward!

Welcome back! As you start your second year in post-primary school, you should be familiar with your school, the various people on the staff and have learned how to be an active member of your school community. What you learned in SPHE last year will have helped you through first year in your new school and throughout the summer holidays.

The year ahead will present you with new challenges and opportunities as you grow and mature and become more independent. This will happen not just in school but in life generally. *Health and Wellbeing: SPHE 2* will help you to deal with all these challenges.

Another year?

Another year?

Another year!

The beginning of a new school year is a good time to think about how things went for you in first year and to look forward to second year and figure out how you might make the most of the year ahead.

Everybody's experience of first year is different and unique to them, so don't worry about what anyone else says or does.

Activity 1

First-year review

Look at the statements below and rate yourself on a scale from 1 to 5, based on how you got on in first year – 1 is 'not so good' and 5 is 'really well'.

	1	2	3	4	5
1 Making new friends	☐	☐	☐	☐	☐
2 My end of year report	☐	☐	☐	☐	☐
3 Participating in class	☐	☐	☐	☐	☐
4 Doing school activities	☐	☐	☐	☐	☐
5 Getting involved in activities outside school	☐	☐	☐	☐	☐
6 Taking more responsibility for myself	☐	☐	☐	☐	☐
7 Managing new challenges	☐	☐	☐	☐	☐
8 Learning from my mistakes	☐	☐	☐	☐	☐
9 Asking for help when I needed it	☐	☐	☐	☐	☐

If I was starting first year again I would change _____

_____

_____

_____

_____

New Year's resolutions

Starting your second year in school is an opportunity for new beginnings. In Activity 1 you identified some things that you might like to have done differently if you were starting off in first year again. Now in Activity 2 you can use your experience to offer advice to new first-year students. This advice will also help you to make some 'New Year's' resolutions for your second year in post-primary school.

KEY WORDS

Resolution

A serious promise or decision that you will do or not do something.

KEY WORDS

Advice

Suggestions about what is good for you to do.

Activity 2 — Hello first years!

Write a letter or email to new first-year students giving them the advice that you would have found useful when you were starting first year. Tell them what you liked and enjoyed about first year, the opportunities it offered and some of the new experiences you had. Write about what you would do differently if you were starting off in first year again, the regrets you have and the opportunities you think you missed. Then write your three main pieces of advice in the space on the right and keep it either in your SPHE folder or in your e-folder.

DO YOUR BEST

FORGET THE REST

My advice for first years is

1 _____

_____

2 _____

_____

3 _____

_____

3   Making the best of your time

Use what came up in Activity 2 to help your class compile a list of the different pieces of advice offered. Discuss the good and bad points of each and then, in the spaces below, write down what your class considers to be the six most helpful pieces of advice for first years and why you think this is so. Then complete the learning log on the opposite page.

Advice

Advice for first years

1
2
3
4
5
6

Create a PowerPoint presentation, illustrating your key pieces of advice for first years and how following the advice will help them. Talk to the first-year SPHE teachers and ask them if you may make a presentation to an SPHE class (your class will have to decide who gives the presentation). Keep your PowerPoint presentation in your e-folder.

Starting off in second year I will

Something I learned about myself in doing these activities was

Ground Rules for Working Together in SPHE

You will remember from SPHE in primary school and from your SPHE classes last year that sometimes you worked alone in class or in pairs or in small groups, very often discussing topics which were quite personal. Doing this requires that you stick to your SPHE 'Class Ground Rules', as they ensure that your class is a safe environment for everyone.

Let's look at what rules you need to guide your work in second year.

Activity

4 Ground rules: Diamond nine

There are ten possible ground rules shown scattered around a diamond nine on page 6 which would make your SPHE class safe and enjoyable for all. In groups of three, discuss each one and why you think it is important. Decide which rule your group thinks is the most important and which is the least important. You can delete the least important one.

Then write the rules into the diamond nine shape:

KEY WORDS

Class ground rules
Statements which make it clear how people should behave and what people can say and do in your class.

- Your number 1 is the rule your group considers to be the most important
- The next two rules are of equal importance and go in the boxes labelled 2
- The next three rules are of equal importance and go in the boxes labelled 3
- The next two rules are of equal importance and go in the boxes labelled 4
- Your number 5 is the rule your group considers to be the least important.

Compare your group's choices with other groups and *decide on the five most important rules* for your SPHE class. Write them down on the *Class Ground Rules* contract on page 7 and sign them to show that you agree to keep them.

Some rules you might like to include

Class Ground Rules

The five ground rules that our class decided are most important in SPHE are:

1 _____

_____

2 _____

_____

3 _____

_____

4 _____

_____

5 _____

_____

While doing Activity 4 one thing I learned about how I work with others is

_____

The rule I will find hardest to keep is

_____

so I promise that I will

_____

Something that will help me keep this rule is

_____

_____

_____

LEARNING LOG

Useful Website
www.kidshealth.org – great website, offering a range of information, hints and tips for teenagers about looking after yourself, in all aspects of your life.

Assessment – Check your learning

Now that you have looked back over your time in first year, make a 'New Year's' resolution to yourself. In your copybook, write down four things you promise yourself you will do to get the most out of second year. For example, now that the novelty of first year has worn off, the challenges of third-year exams are in the distance, so one of your resolutions could be to focus on them.

Review of Unit 1: *Self-Management 1 – Making a New Start*

1 In this unit I learned about _____

_____

_____

2 I think that this will help me when _____

_____

_____

3 In this unit I liked _____

_____

_____

4 In this unit I did not like _____

_____

_____

5 I would like to find out more about _____

_____

_____

6 This unit links with (name another unit in SPHE or another subject) _____

_____

_____

UNIT 1 Self-Management 2 – Looking Ahead!

Learning Outcomes:

This unit helps you to:

1. Set goals and targets for the year ahead ○
2. Learn how to motivate yourself ○
3. Learn how *you* can study effectively ○
4. Explore ways of making decisions. ○

(Tick off as you complete them.)

DESIRE

AMBITION

GOALS

OPPORTUNITY

VISION

Setting Goals and Targets

Now that you have identified some things that you want to do to make the most of second year, let's explore ways of ensuring that you are successful.

A good starting point is learning how to set and work towards achieving specific goals, as this will give you a sense of direction and purpose in your work.

KEY WORDS

Goal
Target
Goal setting
Motivation
Decision

 PowerPoint

What you learn in the activities below can be applied in many other areas of your life, now and into the future.

KEY WORDS

Goal

Something that you are trying to achieve or do.

Target

Something you aim at.

Goal setting

Deciding on a goal and making a plan about how to achieve it.

Activity

1 My goals for the coming year

What would you like to have achieved by this time next year? Write down as many goals as you can think of – looking at all areas of your life. Think about possible achievements in your **personal life**, your **school life**, your favourite subjects, sports and extra-curricular activities, hobbies and with your friends and family. Let your imagination run wild!

Write the goals that you'd like to achieve in the circles on the target board. Put the goal that you think is most important in the middle and the ones that are less important in the other circles.

By this time next year I would like . . .

Activity 2 — Achieving my plans

Now that you have thought about what you'd like to achieve by this time next year, discuss your goals with your classmates and answer the questions below.

1 List two goals that you have in common with your classmates.

_____

_____

2 List two goals that are different from your goals.

_____

_____

3 What or who might help you achieve your goals?

_____

Differences between goals and wishes

Goal: You have control over your goals!

For example, 'I want to improve my fitness', 'I want to get grade B in my next Maths test'.

Wishes: You cannot control all your wishes!

For example, 'I wish I could be in the school musical but I cannot sing – but I can do props'.

> For a wish to become a goal you need a plan.
>
> A goal without a plan is only a wish!

Activity 3 — What's a wish and what's a goal?

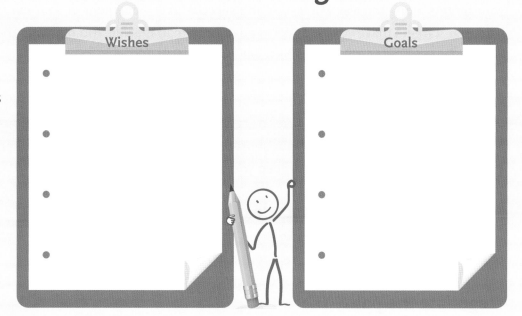

Look back at the words and phrases you have written in the target in Activity 1 and divide them into two groups under the headings 'wishes' and 'goals'. Write them into the two pads.

How many of the things that you hope to achieve are actually goals?

_____

_____

Achieving your goals – you can do it!

Let's look at how you can make a plan to achieve your goals. Having a motto will help you! Remember Barack Obama's motto: 'Yes, we can!' Well your motto is: **YES, I CAN**!

Identify the goal

Make sure your **goal is realistic** and possible to achieve. Write it down or tell somebody about it.

If your goal is long term, you need to break it down into a few short-term goals. For example, your goal might be to get a lead role in the school musical. Your short-term goals would be to identify a part you think would suit you, learn some songs, prepare for the audition and

plan your time so you can practise on your own. These short-term goals are your targets. Reaching your targets along the way will lead to the successful achievement of your overall goal – getting that lead role. Targets make your long-term goal more manageable and reaching them will give you a sense of success along the way which will help to keep you motivated.

Clarify the steps

Work out the steps you need to take to start achieving your goal (or each short-term goal). Write them down. Set a **timeframe** for both your short-term and long-term goals. As you achieve each one, you can mark it off as 'done'. This will keep you motivated too.

Assess the pitfalls or obstacles

Identify the things that might make achieving your goal difficult. If you know what the pitfalls or obstacles are you will be better prepared to work hard and deal with them.

Negotiate the path

Take action and start the journey towards reaching your goal. Check your progress and be prepared to change your plan or targets. Don't forget to reward yourself along the way when you have achieved success.

4

Ava's goal-setting plan

Ava is working towards achieving her dream of getting a place on the under-15 basketball team. Read the steps that Ava takes and apply them to achieving a goal of your own.

Identify the goal

Goal: Ava wants to get on to the under-15 basketball team.

Clarify the steps

To achieve this:

- Ava decides to stay for practice two evenings a week after school

- Ava makes sure her kit is ready each time

- Ava builds up her physical fitness

- Ava talks to the coach and asks for suggestions on how to improve her game

- Ava arranges other times to complete her homework

- Ava works on a healthy eating plan.

Assess the obstacles or pitfalls

Ava find ways to overcome the pitfalls and obstacles she identifies.

Pitfalls/Obstacles	Solutions
Giving up my free time during the week.	I'll build in free time over the weekend.
Finding time to get my homework done.	I'll adjust my weekly homework schedule.
Seeing less of my friends.	I'll arrange to meet them on Saturday and make new friends at basketball.
Watching what I eat and giving up junk food which I like.	I should be doing this anyway to stay healthy!

Negotiate the path

Ava takes action and starts working towards achieving her goal of getting into the team.

By Halloween Ava has had six weeks extra training, feels more physically fit and is eating very healthily. She has a positive attitude, even though she has not made it into the basketball team yet. Ava has learned not to blame others and, most important, she remains motivated to reach her goal.

Select one goal from the ones you listed on the target board in Activity 1 and apply the 'I CAN' steps to it.

I _____

_____

C _____

_____

A _____

_____

N _____

_____

A second goal I would like to achieve this year is

What would help me to achieve this is

Something I learned from the I CAN approach is

What Motivates You?

Having a 'can do' attitude and being motivated to achieve your goals can also ensure success. For example, many factors come into play when it comes to being successful in school. You will have explored some of these in first year – the way you organise your work at home and in school, your study timetable and the **'Three S's' of effective study (stuff, schedule, space)**. Hopefully you will have developed good homework routines and study habits to help to keep you motivated.

Look at the activity below to learn more about how motivation works.

KEY WORDS

Motivation
Something that drives you to do something.

Activity

5 | What motivates Ollie?

▶ Animation

In this activity you will explore what motivation means. Read about Ollie's holiday and then answer the questions below.

| Ollie really wants to go on a holiday where he can learn kitesurfing. | Ollie asks his friends for advice. They tell him to get a part-time job to earn some money. He gets one in his local shop and sends off his passport application form. | Ollie starts looking for a good value kitesurfing holiday online. |

I love 3D!

| Every time Ollie saves €50 from his part-time job, he goes to the cinema as a reward. One day he loses €50 and opens a savings account to keep his money safe. | Ollie finally has enough saved to book the kitesurfing holiday. He heads off for a week and has an amazing time. |

1 What is Ollie's goal?

_____

_____

2 What are the things that helped him achieve his goal?

_____

_____

3 What might prevent Ollie from achieving his goal?

_____

_____

Building blocks of motivation

Motivation is the **desire** to achieve a goal, combined with the **energy** and **commitment** to work towards that goal. It is an inner feeling that drives you towards achieving a result.

Visualising yourself achieving your goal is often a key motivating factor, along with your 'can do' attitude, asking for help and the other building blocks of motivation.

In the wall below you can see the nine factors which will help keep you motivated along the way as you work towards achieving your goal.

BELIEVE YOU CAN AND YOU ARE HALFWAY THERE

1 **Have a clear goal**

2 **Picture yourself**   3 **Plan well**

4 **Ask for help**   5 **Identify your skills**   6 **Learn from your mistakes**

7 **Celebrate small successes**   8 **Keep a positive outlook – a 'can do' attitude**   9 **Be open to encouragement**

6 Ollie's building blocks

Working in pairs or groups, look at Ollie's story again and under each of the factors that keep him motivated below, write an example of how he used it.

1   Having a clear goal (short-term and long-term):

_____

_____

2   Picturing achieving his goal:

_____

_____

3   Making a plan to help him work towards his goal:

_____

_____

4   Asking for help and support:

_____

_____

5   Identifying the people and skills that will help him reach his goal:

_____

_____

6   Learning from his mistakes and not giving up when things go wrong:

_____

_____

7   Celebrating small successes and milestones reached (targets):

_____

_____

8   Keeping a positive outlook and using positive self-talk – 'Yes, I can!':

_____

_____

9   Accepting encouragement along the way:

_____

_____

Motivation – thinking, doing and feeling

Ollie achieved his dream and made his goal a reality because he was motivated. Becoming motivated to work towards achieving a goal, no matter how big or small that goal might be, can be difficult. **Motivation** is affected by what you **think,** what you **do,** how you **feel** and how your **body** is physically reacting.

Sometimes things don't always go according to plan!

7

It's your choice

James has worked hard to get a place on the local football team. After the second match, the coach drops him for another player. There are two possible ways in which James can react. Discuss his two possible responses with a partner and then answer the questions on the opposite page.

Response A

What is James THINKING?	What is James DOING?
• The coach has favourites • I'm better than other people on the team • The coach doesn't like me • I'm no good • It's who you know that counts!	• Complaining about the coach • Blaming himself for not making the team • Taking it out on his friends and family • Sulking • Giving up training • Overeating or drinking.

What is James FEELING?	How is James reacting PHYSICALLY?
• Angry • Rejected • Resentful • Frustrated • Victimised (picked on) • Useless.	• Agitated movements • Finding it hard to sleep • Lack of concentration • Stomach in a knot • Red face – boiling.

Response B

What is James THINKING?	What is James DOING?
• I am slower than some of the others • The coach has nothing against me personally • I will ask the coach what my weak points are and will work on them • I will get back on the team!	• Completing extra fitness training • Working on his speed • Keeping in contact with the coach • Staying in touch with his teammates • Letting the coach know he is interested • Eating healthily.

What is James FEELING?	How is James reacting PHYSICALLY?
• Focused • Involved • A bit angry • Positive • Optimistic.	• Staying relaxed • Sleeping properly • Concentrating better • Able to perform • Fitter.

1 Which response, A or B, would have the better outcome for James?

_____

2 Why do you think this is so?

_____

_____

Important!

If you change the way you **think** about something, the way you **feel** changes too, and so does what you **do**! When James changed the way he thought about his situation and began to look more positively at it, other aspects changed as a result. He worked on his fitness, felt more positive and optimistic and he became healthier.

Describe a time in your own life when you were unhappy with the outcome of a situation, and when what you thought and did was unhelpful. From what you have just learned, suggest how you might have dealt with the situation differently and got a better outcome.

The situation:

_____

_____

What I should have thought:

_____

What I should have done:

_____

How I should have felt:

_____

How I should have reacted physically:

_____

The better outcome would have been:

_____

LEARNING LOG

Making Decisions

You have now learned about the importance of being able to set goals and work towards achieving them. This process involves making decisions at various points along the way, so you need to understand how people make decisions. This is an important life skill. There will be times when the decisions that you make may not be the right ones and you can learn from that too.

Why are my friends doing that?

What should I do?

What am I doing here?

Practice makes perfect!.

PowerPoint

> **KEY WORDS**
>
> **Decision**
> A choice that you make about something after thinking about several possibilities.

Activity 8

Sophie's decision

Sophie has known for some time that things were not good between her mother and father, so she was a bit relieved when they told her that they were going to separate. They both sat Sophie down and explained why they felt this was for the best. The arrangement was that Sophie's younger sister and brother were going to live with their mother but they would still see their dad every week. He wouldn't be living too far away from them. As Sophie was fourteen, her parents asked her to decide where she wanted to live. They knew this wouldn't be an easy decision for Sophie and they were happy to go with whatever she decided was best for her.

Sophie has a decision to make.

Put yourself in Sophie's shoes and describe, in the space below, how you would go about making this decision. Then say what your decision was and why you made it.

To make this decision I would _____

_____

_____

_____

_____

_____

_____

_____

I decided to _____

_____

because _____

_____

_____

How to make decisions

People make decisions in all sorts of ways, using different decision-making styles. Six different decision-making styles that people generally use are listed below. Depending on the decision you are making, you could use one or more of them.

Weigh up the pros and cons
Allow others to influence you
Play safe and take the least risky option
Go with your gut and opt for what feels best
Ask for advice
Do nothing, adopt a 'wait and see' approach

Activity

9 What's your decision-making style?

Read the six decision-making styles again and work out which one you used in Activity 8 for 'Sophie's decision'. Then complete the statements below.

1   In deciding what would be best for Sophie the decision-making style I used was _____

_____

_____

2   Now I think a better way to have made this decision would be _____

_____

_____

BIPED model for making decisions

Sometimes having a model for making decisions is helpful. One model that people use is called the 'BIPED model'. A biped is a creature that can walk on two feet. Making your own decisions means that you can stand on your own two feet and take responsibility for the decisions you make.

B I P E D model – standing on your own two feet!

Identify a decision you have to make. Write it down.

The decision I have to make is:

_____

1　**B**　**Brainstorm** a list of possible options or alternatives. Write everything down.
　　　Possible options are:
_____

2　**I**　Gather **information** about each option and the possible outcomes. Write these down too.

3　**P**　Consider the **pros and cons** (positives and negatives) for each option. Write them down, using a blank page divided into two columns, with pros on one side and cons on the other.

4　**E**　**Evaluate** (weigh up) the alternatives based on your exploration of the pros and cons.

5　**D**　**Decide** on one option, make a plan and carry it out.

When you put your plan into action, don't forget to evaluate the results and learn from them – otherwise you will probably make the same mistakes again and again!

Activity

10　Using the BIPED model

Let's see how you can apply this model to some scenarios. In groups of three, apply the BIPED steps to either Option A or Option B.

Option A: A baby-sitting dilemma

You have recently started baby-sitting your niece to earn some extra money. You have promised your sister that you will babysit on Friday night. Then you realise that it clashes with your dance class and you don't want to miss it as there's a competition in two weeks. Use the BIPED model to help you to decide what to do.

B _____
_____

I _____
_____

P _____
_____

E _____
_____

D _____
_____

Option B: To smoke or not!

Some of your friends recently started smoking cigarettes and are trying to get you to join in. You hate smoking and are also trying to stay fit and healthy to keep your place on the school football team. You still want to be friends with them but they slag you off for not joining in. Use the BIPED model to help you to decide what to do.

B _____

_____

I _____

_____

P _____

_____

E _____

_____

D _____

_____

Assessment – Check your learning

Remember

We all learn from our mistakes

Think of a decision that you made recently that did not have a good outcome. Apply the BIPED model to this decision and see what a better outcome might have been.

My decision _____

_____

Brainstorm options _____

_____

Gather **i**nformation _____

_____

Consider the **p**ros and cons _____

_____

Evaluate alternatives _____

_____

Decide on an option and make a plan _____

_____

From completing this I now understand _____

_____

Review of Unit 1: *Self-Management 2 –*
Looking Ahead!

1 In this unit I learned about _____

_____

_____

2 I think that this will help me when _____

_____

_____

3 In this unit I liked _____

_____

_____

4 In this unit I did not like _____

_____

_____

5 I would like to find out more about _____

_____

_____

6 This unit links with (name another unit in SPHE or another subject) _____

_____

_____

UNIT 1 Self-Management 3 – Learning How to Study

Learning Outcomes:

This unit helps you to:

1. Discover different learning styles ○
2. Identify your own learning style ○
3. Learn how to study effectively ○
4. Practise your study skills. ○

(Tick off as you complete them.)

Study Skills – Learning Styles

In first year, you learned how to organise your school and study timetables and how to manage your time and your study space. In this unit, you will explore different ways of learning and identify how and what helps *you* to learn more effectively. You will learn new skills which will stand to you throughout your life.

VISUAL AUDITORY TACTILE/KINAESTHETIC

The different ways in which people learn are called **learning styles**. Every individual has a preferred learning style and knowing **how you learn best** can help you to make better use of your study time and to learn more efficiently.

There are three basic learning styles. Which one are you?

Visual learners

Visual learners learn by watching and reading. They call up images from the past when they are trying to remember information. They are described as being **'picture smart'** because they picture the way things look.

Auditory learners

Auditory learners learn best by listening. They take information in through their ears and remember facts that are presented in the form of a poem, a song, a melody or a rhyme. As auditory learners don't visualise well, they sometimes have trouble reading. They are described as being **'music smart'**.

Tactile/Kinaesthetic learners

Tactile/kinaesthetic learners learn best through movement and using their hands. They like to find out how things work and are often successful in practical subjects where they can use their hands, e.g. art or design, and in situations where they can move around while they are learning something. They are described as being **'body smart'**.

Complete the Learning Log and then take the quiz.

I think my preferred learning style is

because

LEARNING LOG

Did You Know?

People learn in many different ways and very few people learn using only one style. You can use different learning styles depending on the subject involved. For example, learning a language involves an auditory learning style, while understanding maps in Geography involves a visual learning style and learning through experimental work in the laboratory involves a tactile/kinesthetic learning style.

Activity

1

Quick learning style quiz

Do this quick quiz to check if you have correctly identified your learning style.

For each of the nine questions below tick the answer that seems most like you.

1 I remember things best if:
- **(a)** I write them down and read them back to myself ❑
- **(b)** I make lists of the main points and rewrite them repeatedly ❑
- **(c)** I record the information and listen to it ❑

2 I remember:
- **(a)** Faces ❑
- **(b)** Names ❑
- **(c)** Names and faces, if I can shake hands ❑

3 I like to learn using:
- **(a)** Lab work and demonstrations ❑
- **(b)** Rhyming chants that I make up ❑
- **(c)** Photographs and diagrams ❑

4 When I study I like to:
- **(a)** Sit, walk around and stand some of the time ❑
- **(b)** Use a highlighter to mark the important pieces ❑
- **(c)** Chant the main points to help me memorise them ❑

5 I have trouble remembering information if:
- **(a)** I cannot discuss it in class ❑
- **(b)** I read it and do not talk about it in class ❑
- **(c)** I cannot take notes ❑

6 I study best:
- **(a)** In a group, so I can discuss the information with others ❑
- **(b)** On my own in a quiet place ❑
- **(c)** With one other person, using role-playing games ❑

7 If I am learning about a new mobile phone or camera, I learn best by:
- **(a)** Using the phone or camera ❑
- **(b)** Reading the instructions ❑
- **(c)** Someone telling me about it ❑

8 When I study for a test it helps me if:
- **(a)** I trace pictures, charts and diagrams with my finger ❑
- **(b)** I read aloud ❑
- **(c)** I organise the information into diagrams, spidergrams and flow charts ❑

9 Sometimes when I am studying on my own I will:
- **(a)** Act out information ❑
- **(b)** Draw a picture, showing the process or an event I need to remember ❑
- **(c)** Create songs or rhymes to help me with my homework ❑

Scoring: (Your teacher will help you score the quiz)

Visual _____   Auditory _____   Tactile/Kinaesthetic _____

Result: My preferred learning style is

_____

Activity 2

Class survey – learning styles in your class

When you have worked out your preferred learning style, carry out a survey of the different learning styles in your class. Then work out the following statistics:

In our class ____ % are visual learners

____ % are auditory learners

____ % are tactile/kinaesthetic learners

In your copybook, draw a pie chart like the sample, but using the percentages from your class survey. Then answer the question below.

How well do you know yourself? Is this the same learning style that you identified for yourself in Activity 1?

_____

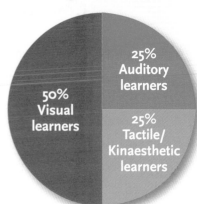

Learning styles sample

How does knowing your learning style help you?

When you know your unique learning style, you can use it to help you study more efficiently. For example, if you are a visual learner you could use a highlighter to mark the important points in your textbook, as this makes the information stand out in a way that appeals to visual learners.

Below are some tips to help you make better use of your study time.

The suggestions in the table will help you to use your preferred learning style to improve the way you study.

Visual learners	Auditory learners	Tactile/Kinaesthetic learners
• Use pictures, charts, maps, and graphs	• Start a study group	• Take frequent study breaks
• Read books with diagrams	• Join a class discussion group	• Move around, pace and stand up while studying
• Watch TV programmes	• Revise by closing your book and saying the main points out loud	• Music, without lyrics, may be helpful
• Use computers and films	• Read your textbooks out loud	• Make posters or charts of the information and put them up in your study area
• Write a story and illustrate it	• Listen to radio programmes	• Try making models, doing the experiment or cooking the dish
• Use colours and highlighters when you are studying	• Turn essay answers into speeches	• Skim through the whole piece before learning the details
• Take notes in class	• Use mnemonics to help you remember facts (see MRS FERG in the next section)	• Use different colours to organise your work
• Have a clear view of the board and teacher		• Write or type out the main points
• Make posters or flow charts of the information and put them up in your study area		• Get involved in role-playing activities
• Study in a quiet place		

Activity 3

My learning style

Now that you have a better understanding of your own learning style, and how you can improve your study habits, compare how you study with students who have the same learning style as you. Write down what you have in common, in terms of your favourite subjects and how you learn.

We all use a range of learning styles but our preferred learning style is the one we use most often. You may not have been aware of yours until now!

_____

_____

_____

LEARNING LOG

Re-read the section on your learning style on page 28. Tick the things you already do while studying and underline the new things you will try to do this week. Write down four things that you now know you can do to help you to learn more effectively.

_____

_____

_____

_____

How to Study: Sharpen your Study Skills

Knowing your learning style, understanding how you learn best and how to organise yourself in preparation for studying effectively are all important points, but it doesn't end there. You must also know how to study! On the following pages you will find out about three different things that will help you.

PowerPoint

KEY WORDS

Study skills

Different ways of managing your learning and making it more efficient.

1 Summarising and mind maps

A mind map is a visual form of note-taking. You can use colours, images, words or symbols to represent information. A mind map helps you reduce the amount of material you have to remember.

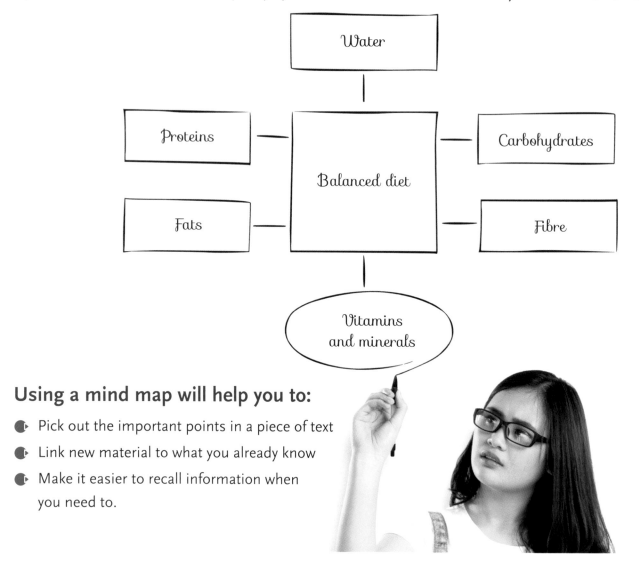

Using a mind map will help you to:

- Pick out the important points in a piece of text
- Link new material to what you already know
- Make it easier to recall information when you need to.

2 Mnemonics

Having a mnemonic is useful when you want to remember a list. To make a mnemonic you use the first letter of each word in your list to make a new word or sentence. This makes it easier for you to remember the information.

Look at the mnemonic below. It will help you to remember the colours of the rainbow in the order in which they appear.

Richard	**Of**	**York**	**Gave**	**Battle**	**In**	**Vain**
Red	Orange	Yellow	Green	Blue	Indigo	Violet

3 Flashcards

To make flashcards you summarise the main points in a topic and write them on cards which you keep for reference. You may have several cards for one topic.

Flashcards are helpful when you are revising before an exam, but you must write them up as you are studying the material.

1/7

Main points

Sub-headings
-
-
-
-
-

Using your new study skills

Let's look at how you can use these three methods to help you study, remember and revise the topic: Living things.

Living things

The study of living things is called biology. Living things are also called organisms. All living organisms are made of cells. Some living organisms consist of only one cell, while others consist of millions of cells.

Living things can be divided into two main groups – animals and plants. The cells of animals do not have a cell wall. The cells of plants do have a cell wall.

In general, living things have seven features. These are called the seven characteristics of living things. They are: movement, respiration (the release of energy from food), sensitivity (reaction to changes in their surroundings), feeding, excretion, reproduction and growth.

1 Movement

Animals can move from place to place. They walk, run, swim or fly.

Plants don't move from place to place but plant parts may move more slowly. Some plants open and close their petals. The sunflower turns its head in response to the sun.

2 Respiration

Both **animals** and **plants** break down food in their cells and get energy to live from that.

3 Sensitivity

Animals respond to changes in their surroundings, including hot or cold temperatures, noise, danger, availability of food and a need for shelter. These responses can be fast or slow.

Plants respond more slowly. Their leaves respond by growing towards the light. Their roots respond to gravity by growing downwards.

4 Feeding

Animals get their food by eating other plants or animals. They do not make their own food. Feeding is also called nutrition.

Plants make their food in a process called photosynthesis. Plants contain a special chemical called chlorophyll so that they can do this.

5 Excretion

Excretion is the removal of the poisonous waste products of chemical reactions from the body.

Animals excrete (get rid of) waste such as salts, water and carbon dioxide.

Plants excrete very little because most of their waste products are used up in other chemical reactions.

6 Reproduction

Reproduction is the making of new living organisms, ensuring that each kind of living organism does not die out or become extinct. Both **animals** and **plants** reproduce in a variety of different ways.

7 Growth

Growth means that the organism gets bigger. Both **animals** and **plants** grow and increase in size.

1 Making a mind map

Read the text again. Highlight the important points and make your mind map.

Living things

The study of living things is called biology. Living things are also called organisms.

All living organisms are made of cells.

Some living organisms consist of only one cell, while others consist of millions of cells.

Living things can be divided into two main groups – animals and plants.

The cells of animals do not have a cell wall.

The cells of plants do have a cell wall.

In general, living things have seven features. These are called the seven characteristics of living things:

1 Movement	4 Feeding
2 Respiration (the release of energy from food)	5 Excretion
3 Sensitivity (reacting to changes in their surroundings)	6 Reproduction
	7 Growth

1   **Movement**

Animals can move from place to place. They walk, run, swim or fly.

Plants don't move from place to place but plant parts may move more slowly. Some plants open and close their petals. The sunflower turns its head in response to the sun.

2   **Respiration**

Both animals and plants break down food in their cells and get energy to live from that.

3   **Sensitivity**

Animals respond to changes in their surroundings, including hot or cold temperatures, noise, danger, availability of food and a need for shelter. These responses can be fast or slow.

Plants respond more slowly. Their leaves respond by growing towards the light. Their roots respond to gravity by growing downwards.

4   **Feeding**

Animals get their food by eating other plants or animals. They do not make their own food. Feeding is also called nutrition.

Plants make their food in a process called photosynthesis. Plants contain a special chemical called chlorophyll so that they can do this.

5   **Excretion**

Excretion is the removal of the poisonous waste products of chemical reactions from the body.

Animals excrete (get rid of) waste such as salts, water and carbon dioxide.

Plants excrete very little because most of their waste products are used up in other chemical reactions.

6   **Reproduction**

Reproduction is the making of new living organisms, ensuring that each kind of living organism does not die out or become extinct. Both animals and plants reproduce in a variety of different ways.

7   **Growth**

Growth means that the organism gets bigger. Both plants and animals grow and increase in size.

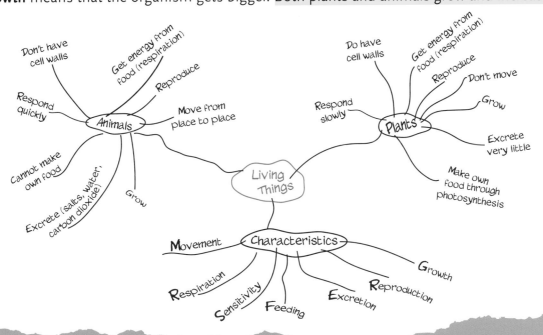

2 Mnemonics

To help you to remember the 'seven characteristics of living things' you can make a mnemonic by picking out the key words and making a sentence out of the first letter of each word, e.g. MRS FERG.

Movement

Respiration (the release of energy from food)

Sensitivity (reacting to changes in their surroundings)

Feeding

Excretion

Reproduction

Growth

MRS FERG

3 Flashcards

Flashcards for 'Living things' might look like this:

Living Things   1/6

* Living things are called organisms.
* All living organisms are made of cells.
* Some living organisms consist of only one cell, others consist of millions of cells.
* Living things can be divided into two main groups – animals and plants.
* The cells of animals do not have a cell wall.
* The cells of plants do have a cell wall.
* Living things have seven common characteristics/features.

Seven characteristics   2/6
/features of living things

Movement

Respiration (the release of energy from food)

Sensitivity (reacting to changes in their surroundings)

Feeding

Excretion

Reproduction

Growth

MRS FERG

Movement   3/6
& Respiration

Movement

Animals can move from place to place – walk, run and fly.

Plants don't move from place to place, but plant parts may move slowly e.g. open/close their petals or leaves.

Respiration

The release of energy from food.

Animals and **plants** carry out respiration (respire).

Sensitivity   4/6
& Feeding

Sensitivity – the response to changes in environment.

Animals can respond quickly or slowly.

Plants respond very slowly.

Feeding – is called nutrition.

Food is necessary to live.

Animals do not make their own food. They eat plants and/or animals.

Plants make their food by photosynthesis. A chemical called chlorophyll is responsible for photosynthesis.

Excretion   5/6

Excretion – the removal of the poisonous waste products of chemical reactions.

Animals excrete wastes such as salts and carbon dioxide.

Plants excrete CO_2 and H_2O (carbon dioxide and water)

Reproduction   6/6
& Growth

Reproduction – the making of new living organisms.

Both animals and plants reproduce in various ways.

Growth – means that the organism gets bigger.

Both plants and animals grow.

Remember

If you are a visual learner you will find making mind maps helpful when you want to remember information.	If you are an auditory learner, using mnemonics will be the best way for you to remember information. Repeat the mnemonic aloud until you can remember it. But make sure you also remember what each of the letters in the mnemonic stands for!	If you are a tactile/kinaesthetic learner, moving around may help you to remember the information. You could also use different colours from paragraph to paragraph to organise your work.

Assessment – Check your learning

Practice makes perfect

Choose a short piece from one of your textbooks and apply the skills you have just learned to:

- Summarise it
- Write the main points on a flashcard
- Make a mind map showing the main points
- Teach it to a small group or to your class.
- Invent a good mnemonic

Keep your work in your SPHE folder or e-folder. Summarise what you learned from each part of this activity in the space below.

1 Summary: _____

    _____

2 Mind map: _____

    _____

3 Mnemonic : _____

    _____

4 Flashcard: _____

    _____

Useful Websites

www.howtostudy.com – offers useful information to help you to study more effectively

Review of Unit 1: *Self-Management 3 – Learning How to Study*

1. In this unit I learned about _____
_____
_____

2. I think that this will help me when _____
_____
_____

3. In this unit I liked _____
_____
_____

4. In this unit I did not like _____
_____
_____

5. I would like to find out more about _____
_____
_____

6. This unit links with (name another unit in SPHE or another subject) _____
_____
_____

UNIT 1 — Self-Management 4 – Being Safe

Learning Outcomes:

This unit helps you to:

1. Take more responsibility for your own safety
2. Contribute towards making your home a safer place
3. Understand how to be vigilant on a farm and avoid accidents
4. Learn the skills of water safety
5. Discover more about being safe in cyberspace.

(Tick off as you complete them.)

KEY WORDS

Safety

Hazard

Cyber safety

Keeping Safe

Knowing how to keep safe is an important part of becoming independent. As you get older and more mature, you learn how to take responsibility for yourself and for your personal safety. Last year in *Health and Wellbeing: SPHE 1* you explored the issues of fire safety, road safety, personal safety and cyber safety. This year you will examine safety at home, on the farm and in the water, and learn more about how to stay safe in cyberspace.

KEY WORDS

Safety
A condition of being safe – when a person is free from danger, risk or injury.

Safety in your home

Everyone knows that accidents can and do happen but many people don't realise that they are more likely to happen in the home than anywhere else. Some important points to remember are:

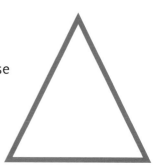

- Children up to the age of five and older people are the most likely to have an accident at home

- Choking, suffocation, burns, scalds and poisonings are some of the typical accidents in the home, with children under five particularly vulnerable to having them

- Trips and falls are the most common kind of accidents in the home

- Boys are more at risk than girls.

KEY WORDS

Hazard
Anything that increases the risk of someone having an accident.

There are potential hazards in every home, including hot water, open fireplaces, unlocked presses (e.g. medicine cabinet) and household cleaners. Other hazards include open or unprotected stairs, rugs and frayed carpets on the floor, sharp knives, water on the floor and so on. Let's explore this further.

Activity

1 A safe house

There are three generations of people living in the house opposite – an elderly granny, a mother and father and their two children, aged two and fifteen. In pairs, study the rooms in the house and answer the questions below. Then complete the Learning Log.

1. Identify four possible hazards in each room and mark them with a red triangle on the picture. Then write them below.

   _____

   _____

   _____

   _____

2. Think about the different ages of the people living in the house and what might make the house an unsafe place for each person. Decide what you could do to make this home a safer place for the five people living there. Write your answer below.

   _____

   _____

   _____

   _____

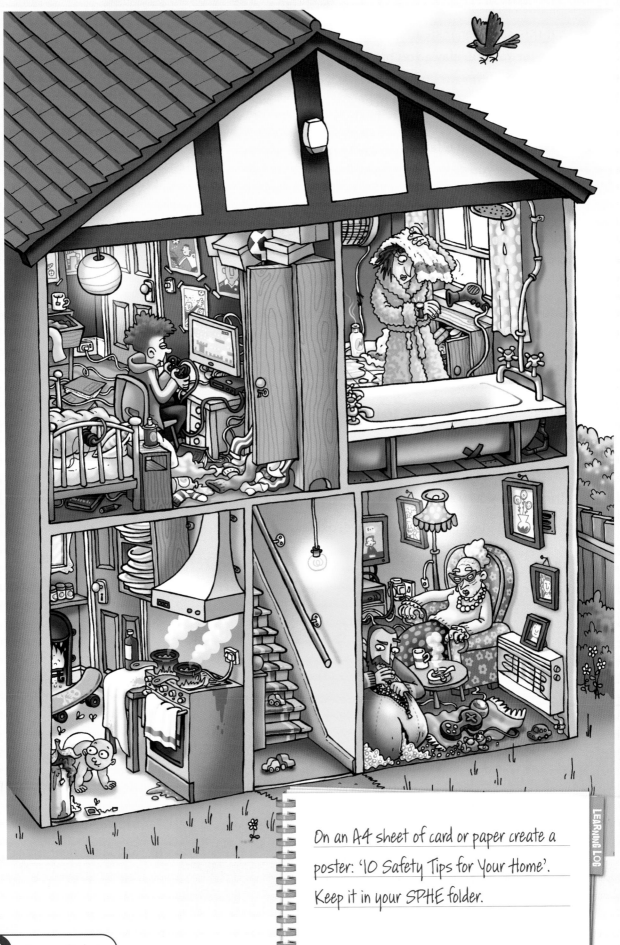

On an A4 sheet of card or paper create a poster: '10 Safety Tips for Your Home'. Keep it in your SPHE folder.

PowerPoint

Safety on the farm

Imagine that this summer, instead of going to the seaside for your holidays, you have been invited to stay with your cousins on their farm in the country. You haven't been there for years but you have happy memories of holidays on the farm when you were younger so you are excited about returning! You are also a bit worried, though, as you have heard that twenty-one people died in farm accidents the year before and that every year thousands more are injured in accidents that could have been prevented.

You decide to find out about the type of dangers you could face while you are on your cousin's farm.

Potential hazards on the farm

- Farm machinery, e.g. tractors, trailers and combine harvesters
- Animals
- Slurry pits – risk of drowning and and being poisoned by fumes, as one breath can kill
- Electricity, e.g. power lines
- Chemicals, e.g. fuels, fertilisers and weedkillers

- Water, e.g. water tanks, waste water, abandoned water wells
- Grain storage plants
- Farm equipment, e.g. ladders, tyres and forks
- Unsuitable clothing, e.g. workers dressed in long coats or poor footwear
- Smoking near fuel, hay or straw.

Activity

2

Spot the hazards

Look at the picture of your cousin's farm below. Working with another student, identify the hazards and mark each one with a red triangle.

LEARNING LOG

Write a list of the 'Top 5 tips for teenagers who are visiting a farm', telling them about the potential hazards and how to keep safe while they are there.

Useful Websites

www.farmsafety4kids.net – games and quizzes on how to stay safe on a farm

www.agrikids.ie – useful tips on farm safety

www.iws.ie – loads of information on water safety

BE ALERT!
BE AWARE!
STAY ALIVE!

Safety in the water

People often think that if they can swim they are safe enough in the water. Sadly, this is not true and each year people die by drowning on beaches and in pools, rivers and lakes. Many of these deaths could have been prevented. In 2015 alone eighty-nine people died by *accidental drowning* in Ireland. Hundreds more were rescued by lifeguards on duty and survived because the lifeguard was able to give CPR (cardiopulmonary resuscitation) and/or first aid.

You should know how to keep yourself and others safe while you are in the water. Check out the fourteen steps for safe swimming on the Irish Water Safety website (www.iws.ie) and all the other useful information they have about keeping safe while you are in the water.

WARNING: Only swim where you see a lifeguard on duty.

Activity 3

Safe swimming

 PowerPoint

In pairs, look at the ten steps for safe swimming below and then study the cartoons on page 44. See if you can match the cartoons with the correct message on safe swimming. The messages are jumbled up! Insert the correct cartoon letters in the boxes below.

1 Don't swim alone

If you get into difficulty and someone is with you they can help, or run and get help. If you have an accident they would have more details about what happened, e.g. last place you were sighted, your injuries and so on.

2 Don't swim just after eating

You should wait at least one hour after you've eaten before going swimming. You are less likely to suffer from cramp if your body has had a chance to digest your food.

3 Don't swim when you're hot or tired

Your body is less able to cope with extreme coldness when you are hot or tired. Your body temperature may drop suddenly, leading to shock or hypothermia.

4 Don't swim in strange places

You may not be aware of the dangers, such as currents, tides, riptides, marine life and submerged objects, if you don't know the place and the hazards are not signposted.

5 Don't swim out after a drifting object

You might think the object (e.g. beach ball, airbed, etc.) is closer than it actually is and you are likely to get exhausted as you try to swim back to shore.

6 Don't stay in the water too long

If you get too cold it will impair your judgement and you may suffer from hypothermia.

7 Swim parallel to the shore

Make sure you are in sight of the shore so if you get tired, someone can help you and you can get out of the water more easily.

8 Never use air mattresses

They can be picked up by the wind and blown out to sea or you can drift out to sea on them without even being aware of it!

9 Pay attention to signs on the beach

You should always read signs near water, as they can include warning signs about e.g. rocks, dangerous swimming areas and so on.

10 Learn to use equipment before trying it out

You need to make sure that you are competent in its use to avoid getting into difficulty in the water.

© Irish Water Safety Association

Think about the places that you swim, whether it is in the sea, in a river or in a lake, and write down five things that you can do to ensure that people are safe when they swim there. Use information from the IWSA website (www.iws.ie) to help you. Think about skills you could begin to develop, e.g. signing up for a lifesaving or CPR training course.

KEY WORDS

Cyber Safety
Keeping safe and being responsible while you are online.

Cyber safety – safety online

PowerPoint

Cyberspace has been compared to a large city with different routes into and out of it, e.g. mobile phones, laptops, tablets and games consoles. These are just some of the forms of ICT (information and communications technology) in use today, by people of all ages. As with all big cities, it is important to know how to keep yourself safe when you are out and about on the Internet.

Activity 4

ICT and me

1. Brainstorm how you and your family and friends use various forms of ICT. What are they used for? How often are they used? Do you use them to watch, listen or play something, or to talk to people? Write as many as you can think of below.

Remember

These are useful tools, but can be open to abuse. Handle with care.

2 Think of a typical day and how much time you spend on any ICT device. Write in the amount of time you spend, e.g. 30 minutes on PlayStation, 60 minutes on mobile phone and so on. Work out the total for each device for every day of the week and write them in the space below. Your times may be very different at weekends!

_____

_____

_____

LEARNING LOG

The main form of ICT that I use is

I use this mainly for

A concern that I sometimes have when using my phone/games machine/computer is that

To keep myself safe in cyberspace I

Privacy in cyberspace

In our digital world it is sometimes difficult to identify the risks involved when you use different forms of ICT. You share information with other people on an ongoing basis and much of this information remains in cyberspace forever. Knowing how to protect your privacy is one way of keeping yourself safe.

Every time you go online you leave a trail! You don't see it happening, but what you do online is tracked by people who might use your information for their own purposes.

46

5   Protecting your privacy

In groups of four, discuss questions 1–5 below and then complete the statements 6–8.

1   Why is your privacy important?

2   What happens when you don't keep important things private?

3   How do you keep things private in the 'real' world?

4   How do you keep information private in the online world?

5   How do you know when, and if, information about you is being shared online?

6   The difference between keeping things private in the real world as opposed to the digital world for me is _____

_____

7   Information I would want to keep private online includes _____

_____

8   Information I would be happy to share online includes _____

_____

and it depends on _____

_____

Did You Know?

Your **browser** (e.g. Mozilla Firefox, Google Chrome, Microsoft Internet Explorer, Apple Safari) remembers the pages you visited for weeks afterwards and sometimes remembers your passwords. Your **search engine** (e.g. Google, Bing, Yahoo) remembers words you used in the past and offers you suggestions based on some key words. **Web pages** you visit often post advertisements for items which are like the ones you bought on other websites.

KEY WORDS

Digital footprint

A trail of information you create while using the Internet, including the websites you visit, emails you send and information you give to online services.

Sharing information online – what happens when you post?

Step 1 Think about the last piece of information you shared with one friend on social media. What did you share? A photo, song or comment?

Step 2 Now think about how many people your friend might share your information with, say twenty more friends.

Step 3 Now assume that those twenty friends also have twenty friends and that they all share your photo, song or comment. How many people will now see what you first shared with one person?

Step 4 And on it goes! Friends of friends of friends keep sharing.

This is how information can be shared and it explains how YouTube clips **'go viral'** and are seen by thousands of people in a short time! For example, in 2016 a YouTube video about cyberbullying by Irish teenager Luke Culhane went viral and has been viewed more than 723,500 times.

Activity
6   Your digital footprint

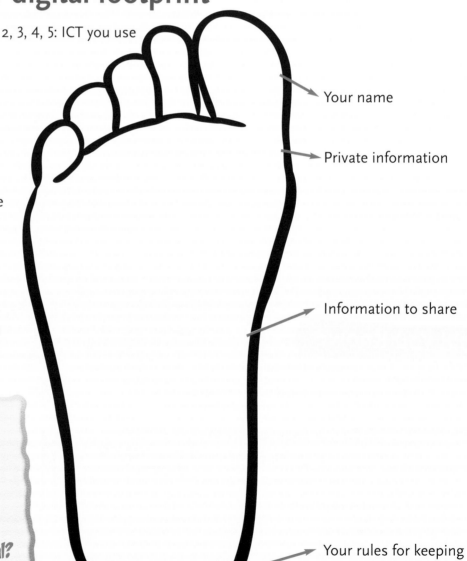

2, 3, 4, 5: ICT you use

Your name

Private information

Information to share

Your rules for keeping safe online

Using what you have learned and the 'Rules for Safe Surfing' to help you, fill in the different parts of your digital footprint below.

Big toe: write in your name

Toes two, three, four and five: write in forms of ICT you use (e.g. mobile, laptop, tablet, MP3, etc.).

Along the foot: write down the information as shown on the footprint.

THINK
Before You
POST
True? Hurtful? Illegal?
Necessary? Kind?

Rules for safe surfing

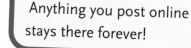

- Only use your mobile phone to talk to people you know

- Make sure your password is 'strong' (use a mix of symbols, numbers and letters) and never tell it to anyone

- Never give personal information to anyone online as some websites may access your personal information without you knowing

- Use a 'screen name' so strangers can't identify who you are

- Only post things you are happy for other people to see and know about you

- Think about setting up a private chat room for you and your close friends

- Never agree to meet a new online friend in person as they may not be who they say they are

- Don't buy anything online without permission from your parents/guardian(s)

- Never say anything online that you wouldn't say offline

- Never reply to mean or hurtful messages; instead, block the sender

- Get advice before opening an email from an unknown sender.

ThinkB4uClick!

Assessment – Check your learning

Write a rap

In groups of three, write a rap on the theme of either water safety or cyber safety. If you need some help, ask your teacher to search YouTube for 'how to write a rap' so that you can get some useful tips before you start. All the groups in your class have to perform their rap. Then have a class vote and decide which rap gets the message across in the best way. You should have a reason for your choice!

Useful Websites

www.childnet.com – a UK website with useful information and advice on key Internet safety issues and interactive games that challenge you to be a responsible digital citizen

www.kidshealth.org – in the teen section there are some great tips on Internet safety

Review of Unit 1: *Self-Management 4 – Being Safe*

1. In this unit I learned about _____

_____

_____

2. I think that this will help me when _____

_____

_____

3. In this unit I liked _____

_____

_____

4. In this unit I did not like _____

_____

_____

5. I would like to find out more about _____

_____

_____

6. This unit links with (name another unit in SPHE or another subject) _____

_____

_____

UNIT **2** How I See Myself and Others

Learning Outcomes:

This unit helps you to:

1 Get to know yourself a little bit better ⃝

2 Explore ways of enhancing your self-esteem and that of others ⃝

3 Understand how your self-esteem and self-confidence contribute to your emotional wellbeing ⃝

4 Discover the benefits of self-acceptance and self-awareness. ⃝

(Tick off as you complete them.)

Your Emotional Health

In first year you learned that many factors contribute to your general health and wellbeing and especially to your emotional health. You also learned how to look after aspects of your mental and emotional health, including how to express your feelings and respect the feelings of others. Feeling good about yourself and helping others to feel good about themselves are essential ingredients in making sure that you have good emotional health.

> ## KEY WORDS
>
> **Self-esteem**
> Self-confidence
> Emotional wellbeing
> Self-awareness
> **Self-acceptance**
> Compliment

Self-esteem and self-confidence

DREAMS
HOPE FAITH
SELF-ESTEEM
CONFIDENCE
MOTIVATION
INDEPENDENCE
ACHIEVEMENT
CREATIVITY
TRUST LOVE
DESIRE
THRIVE

You may have heard these words before but do you remember what they mean and why they are important? Read the definitions in the Key Words box to refresh your memory.

> ## KEY WORDS
>
> Self-esteem
> How much you value yourself.
> Self-confidence
> How sure you are about yourself.

Let's look at how you can build your own self-esteem and self-confidence and that of other people.

Self-esteem

The word 'esteem' has to do with how much you value something. So 'self-esteem' is about how much you value yourself and how worthwhile and capable you feel.

How I feel about myself as a person.

People with healthy levels of self-esteem:

- Have a realistic view of themselves and think people like them
- Accept their weaknesses and celebrate their good qualities, but don't think they are better than other people
- Are prepared to take risks and try new things without being afraid of failure.

Self-esteem is not fixed. It can change depending on the way you think. Thinking about yourself in a positive way can enhance your self-esteem and make you feel better about yourself.

Self-confidence

Self-confidence is related to self-esteem but it is slightly different. Confidence means feeling sure of yourself, so self-confidence is having a belief in yourself and in your ability to do something well. It is especially important when you are facing new challenges and new situations.

Building self-confidence is important if you want to succeed. Sportspeople use psychologists to help them boost their confidence and self-belief.

CONFIDENCE IS LIKE A MUSCLE: THE MORE YOU USE IT, THE STRONGER IT GETS.

Activity 1

This is me – promoting a sense of your own wellbeing

1 Make a collage about yourself, using pictures, photographs, symbols, drawings and words. You can use the statements below to guide you in building a true picture of who you are. Spend a few minutes thinking about this before you start. Keep your collage in your SPHE folder.

Guiding statements
🔊 Something I like about myself is . . .   🔊 A hope I have is . . .

🔊 Something I like about myself is . . .

🔊 An interest or hobby I have is . . .

🔊 Something I appreciate about my appearance is . . .

🔊 Something I am good at is . . .

🔊 Something I'd like to change is . . .

🔊 A hope I have is . . .

🔊 A talent/gift I have is . . .

🔊 A difficulty/challenge I have overcome is . . .

🔊 Something I am proud of is . . .

🔊 An aim/ambition I have is . . .

2 When you have finished, talk about your collage with one or two other students. Share only as much as you feel comfortable discussing.

3 Think about what it was like doing the collage.

  (a) How did you decide what to include or exclude about yourself?

    _____

  (b) Why might you have left some things out and included other things about yourself?

    _____

4 Complete the sentences below.

  (a) The part of this activity I liked best was _____ because _____

    _____

  (b) The part I found easiest was _____ because _____

    _____

  (c) Something I found challenging was _____ because _____

    _____

  (d) I found talking to my classmates about my collage was _____ because _____

    _____

  (e) Something I learned about myself while doing this activity is _____

    _____

    _____

Your Emotional Wellbeing

The collage activity gave you a chance to think about what you are like as a person. Activities like this will help you to appreciate yourself a bit more, which will improve your emotional wellbeing, enhancing your self-esteem and self-confidence.

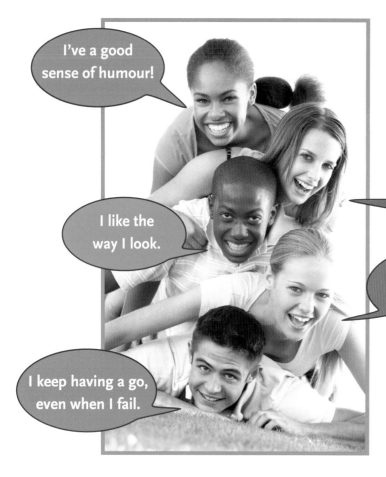

I've a good sense of humour!

I like the way I look.

Some sad things have happened to me but I've found the strength to bounce back.

I get on well with people.

I keep having a go, even when I fail.

Building blocks of emotional wellbeing

Self-esteem

Self-awareness

Self-acceptance

Self-esteem: self-awareness and self-acceptance

An important factor in building your self-esteem is your **self-awareness**, which involves:

- Knowing how you see yourself as a person
- Appreciating your strengths and weaknesses
- Understanding what motivates you and makes you happy
- Being aware of how you relate to your friends and family
- Knowing what you want in your life and being able to make decisions about it.

Self-acceptance comes from your self-awareness. Understanding who you are, and respecting and accepting yourself is an ongoing process throughout your life.

Sometimes it is difficult to change. For example, if you are not good at sports and can accept that you will never make the school tennis team then you can move on and concentrate on what you are good at. If you do this your self-esteem is likely to be healthy, leading to improved emotional wellbeing.

Let's see how we can promote a sense of wellbeing in others.

Promoting emotional wellbeing in others

Making the collage in Activity 1 gave you a chance to think positively about who you are as a person. Now we will explore how you can help other people to feel good about themselves. One way of doing this is to compliment them, by saying something nice about, for example, what they are wearing, their new hairstyle, their helpful attitude and so on.

Activity 2

Feeling good

1. In your copybook, write down three examples of the different *ways* people give compliments to one another.

2. Discuss the different ways with two of your classmates and add in any new ideas that they may have had. Draw a circle around the one that you like best.

Compliments – a two-way process

Giving and receiving compliments is a two-way process. It makes both people feel good about themselves.

Some people feel uncomfortable when they get a compliment and they brush it off by saying something negative. It would be better if they just said, 'thank you', as being able to give and receive compliments helps to build a person's self-esteem and emotional wellbeing.

How can I make my classmates feel good about themselves?

Activity

3

PowerPoint

Giving and receiving compliments

Get into a group with five classmates. Write your name on the label on the gift box. Then pass your textbook to the person on your right and take the textbook passed to you on the left. In one of the balloons write a compliment about the student whose name is on the box. The compliments might be about how they are as a friend, a skill/talent they have, their appearance or how they help others. Keep passing the textbooks around your group, writing in compliments, until you get your textbook back. Then read your compliments and complete the statements below.

When I read the compliments from my classmates, I felt _____

_____

_____

When I was writing compliments about others, I felt _____

_____

_____

Tips for giving and receiving compliments

Giving a compliment	Receiving a compliment
Make eye contact with the person you are complimenting.	Look at the person who is complimenting you.
Say their name.	Listen to the compliment and accept it graciously – don't brush it off.
Use a happy tone of voice.	Use a happy tone of voice.
Compliment them in a way that shows you mean it; be honest and not patronising.	Say 'thank you' and possibly talk about how the compliment made you feel.

LEARNING LOG

Read all the compliments your group wrote about you in Activity 3 again and write your favourite one below. (Remember, many people feel embarrassed writing down good things about themselves!) When your turn comes to read out your compliment for the class, start your statement with the words: I am.

Assessment – Check your learning

A gratitude diary

Keeping a gratitude diary is a great way to improve your self-esteem and self-confidence – and your overall emotional health. It can also help you to keep a positive outlook on life, even when times are tough. Some people write a few lines in their diary every night, as they look back over their day.

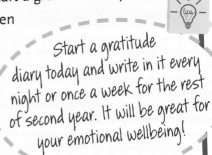

Gratitude list :

Using what you have learned about yourself in the last few activities, start a gratitude diary or just use a blank page and write six or seven lines on things in your life that you are grateful for. Nobody will see this except you! Think about the people around you, the things you have, your skills, interests, abilities, and the opportunities you have for meeting friends and having fun or just hanging out.

Start a gratitude diary today and write in it every night or once a week for the rest of second year. It will be great for your emotional wellbeing!

Useful Websites

www.wikihow.com – search for useful tips on how to start and keep a gratitude diary or journal

www.yourmentalhealth.ie – information and advice on how to improve your awareness and understanding of emotional health

Review of Unit 2: *How I See Myself and Others*

1 In this unit I learned about _____

_____

_____

2 I think that this will help me when _____

_____

_____

3 In this unit I liked _____

_____

_____

4 In this unit I did not like _____

_____

_____

5 I would like to find out more about _____

_____

_____

6 This unit links with (name another unit in SPHE or another subject) _____

_____

_____

UNIT 3
Being an Adolescent

Learning Outcomes:

This unit helps you to:

1. Understand that growing and changing is a normal part of life ⭘

2. Review the physical, social, emotional and psychological changes which occur during adolescence ⭘

3. Appreciate that we are all individual and all different ⭘

4. See the world through the eyes of someone who is LGBT. ⭘

(Tick off as you complete them.)

Physical changes – how different parts of your body **change**

Social changes – how your friendships and relationships **change**

Emotional changes – how your feelings for different people, friends and family **change**

Psychological changes – how your thinking processes **change**

KEY WORDS

Difference
Conform
Sexual orientation

In first year, you were coping with a lot of changes in your life. Moving from primary to post-primary school when you are also making the transition from childhood to adolescence involves all sorts of challenges. Last year you looked in detail at the different changes that take place during puberty. You learned that these changes happen on a few different levels – physical, social, emotional and psychological. All these changes are interlinked and each one impacts on the other, a bit like a jigsaw.

Activity 1

How have you changed?

In the jigsaw below write down the changes that you can remember learning about last year. Write the changes that specifically apply to girls in one colour and the ones that specifically apply to boys in a different colour or signify the changes with male and female gender symbols.

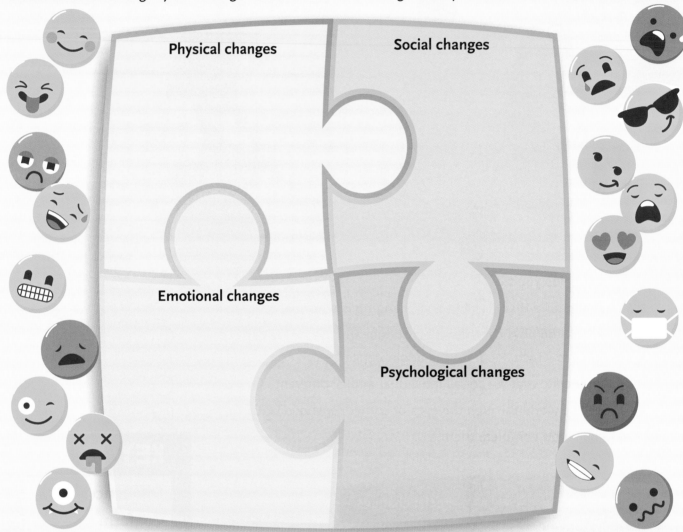

When you have written in all the changes that you can remember, check with your classmates and your teacher and add any you may have forgotten. Then answer the questions below.

1 Which part of your jigsaw has most changes listed on it?

_____

2 Why do you think this is so?

_____

3 Which do you think is more common – changes that boys and girls have in common or changes that are unique to boys and to girls?

_____

4 What does this tell you about boys and girls at puberty?

_____

1 Describe two ways in which these changes might impact on boys and girls at this stage of their lives. Think about how they might feel about themselves and about their relationships with friends and family.

2 Apart from all the different changes which young people experience, what other concerns might they have?

3 Sometimes adolescence can be a challenging time for young people but there is always help at hand. Who are the people you could turn to for help and how would you contact them? Think about people in your school, at home or in some other area of your life.

Being Different or Wanting to Conform

Every person is unique and each of you experiences the changes at puberty and adolescence in a different way. Sometimes it is difficult to be either ahead of your peers or behind them when these changes are taking place. If this happens, you can feel very different from everyone else. This might not be a comfortable place to be.

KEY WORDS

Difference
The way in which people or things are not the same.

KEY WORDS

Conform
To behave in a way that most people in your group or society find acceptable.

Activity 2

Taking a stand – easy or difficult?

As you become more independent you may find yourself in situations where you feel under pressure to conform to what other people think or expect of you. It can be difficult to 'stand on your own two feet' at times like these. Maybe there's pressure for you to smoke, skip school, get a tattoo or body piercing, dress in a particular way or express a particular opinion. Think about a situation like this and discuss the four questions below with two of your classmates and then write down your answers.

1 Describe a situation when you were with a group of people who were doing something or giving opinions that were different from what you thought or wanted to do.

_____

_____

2 How did you feel about it at the time?

_____

_____

3 What did you decide to do or say?

_____

_____

4 If you decided to 'stand on your own two feet' why did you do that and how did you feel afterwards? Were you happy you made that decision or did you regret it? Why?

_____

_____

_____

_____

Feeling different

Sometimes it's difficult to be different. We can often feel pressure from society, the media, our friends and family to conform in a certain way. For example, advertisements that always feature very thin models can make young girls feel that they should also be that skinny. Sometimes we go along with other people because we don't want to appear different and we want to belong.

Being different can be especially difficult when it comes to our sexuality. Let's look at Kyle's story.

Activity

3

Kyle's lifeline

Read the life story of fourteen-year-old Kyle below, from when he was born to the present day. You will see that along the way Kyle has been influenced by outside factors such as his family, his friends, the media and his peer group. Look at the questions at the end and discuss your thoughts with two others before completing them. You will explore this further in Strand 3.

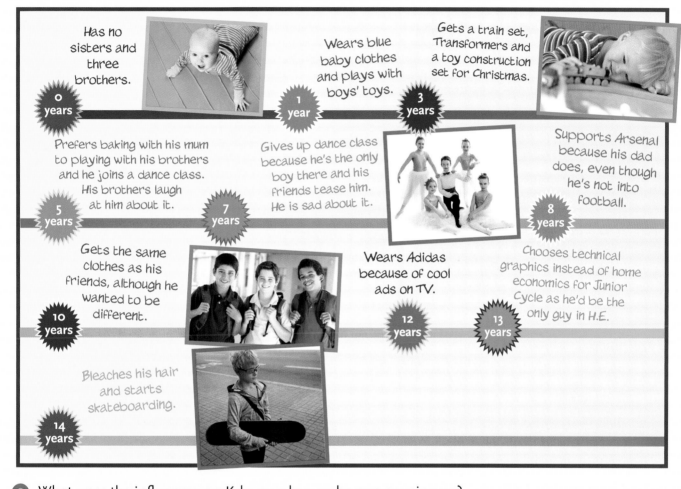

Has no sisters and three brothers.

0 years

Wears blue baby clothes and plays with boys' toys.

1 year

Gets a train set, Transformers and a toy construction set for Christmas.

3 years

Prefers baking with his mum to playing with his brothers and he joins a dance class. His brothers laugh at him about it.

5 years

Gives up dance class because he's the only boy there and his friends tease him. He is sad about it.

7 years

Supports Arsenal because his dad does, even though he's not into football.

8 years

Gets the same clothes as his friends, although he wanted to be different.

10 years

Wears Adidas because of cool ads on TV.

12 years

Chooses technical graphics instead of home economics for Junior Cycle as he'd be the only guy in H.E.

13 years

Bleaches his hair and starts skateboarding.

14 years

1. What were the influences on Kyle, as a boy, as he was growing up?

_____

_____

2. Do you think these influences were positive or negative? Why?

_____

_____

3. How might these influences have affected Kyle as he became a teenager?

_____

_____

4. How has your identity as a boy or girl been influenced by your family, friends and the media as you were growing up?

_____

_____

Feeling that you are different from others can be tough at times. In first year, you learned what some of the words associated with a person's sexual orientation mean. Revise these words again and then read Ger's story below.

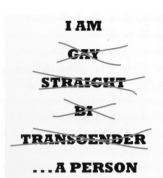

I AM
~~GAY~~
~~STRAIGHT~~
~~BI~~
~~TRANSGENDER~~
...A PERSON

 **Animation**

Activity 4

Ger's story

Read through Ger's story on your own and then discuss the questions on page 65 with two or three others and complete the answers.

Ger seems like a typical fifteen-year-old who does the usual things. He goes to school, plays sports, hangs out with friends and listens to music. But Ger is straight and he lives in a world where everyone else is lesbian, gay, bisexual or transgender (LGBT) – his friends, teachers, neighbours, and the businesspeople, celebrities and politicians are all LGBT too. Ger has heard about a few straight people but they are not really accepted. They are often excluded and people snigger and say hurtful things to them.

Recently a referendum was passed and the law has been changed to allow straight people to marry. Some people don't like that.

Last month a girl in sixth year dropped out of school because she was being bullied and teased for being straight. Some of the boys in Ger's class have boyfriends and some of the girls have girlfriends and they seem to be very happy. He would love a life like that too, but it's not that simple.

Ger is unhappy, feels different from everyone else and is becoming increasingly uncomfortable and worried about being straight in a world where most other people are LGBT. There is no one that Ger feels comfortable enough to share this secret with, so he feels alone and doesn't know what to do. His parents and brother never talk about things like this, and Ger is afraid to bring it up because the comments they made during the referendum have made him concerned about their negative reaction.

Ger knows that there are people in school who are there to help with things like this and he could tell a close friend but he feels that talking about it could be risky. Ger decides not to tell anyone and to just live with his secret, although sometimes he thinks it might be easier to pretend to be gay.

1. How, do you think, does this story mirror the experiences of gay, lesbian, bisexual or transgender young people?

_____

_____

2. How does Ger feel?

_____

_____

3. Why, do you think, does Ger feel like this?

_____

_____

4. Imagine you are Ger. How would it feel if you had to keep something as important as your sexuality a secret? How would it affect your life and your friendships?

_____

_____

5. What do you remember about the first time you heard that some people were LGBT? What did you think?

_____

_____

6. Why do you think LGBT people are bullied or harassed?

_____

_____

7. If a friend told you that he or she was gay, lesbian, bisexual or transgender, how would you feel? What would you say to them? What could you do?

_____

_____

LEARNING LOG

In groups of three, discuss what your school needs to do to make it a more welcoming, inclusive and safer place for someone like Ger. Think about what facilities are in place already and what else might help. Write your answer below.

_____

_____

_____

Useful Websites

www.belongto.org – an organisation that offers support to LGBT young people

www.barnardos.ie – the teen help section provides support and advice to teenagers as part of Barnardo's aim to make Ireland a safer place for children and teenagers

www.childline.ie – provides support and a listening ear to children and young people up to the age of eighteen

Assessment – Check your learning

Write a letter to your ten-year-old self. Describe how you have changed and how your life has altered over the past four years. Write down the things you like about the way you are now and maybe mention some of the things you are not happy with. Talk about how you have coped with adolescence and about some of the difficulties you have experienced. Feel free to include anything else that comes to mind. Keep the letter in your e-folder or in your SPHE folder.

Review of Unit 3: *Being an Adolescent*

1 In this unit I learned about _____

_____

_____

2 I think that this will help me when _____

_____

_____

3 In this unit I liked _____

_____

_____

4 In this unit I did not like _____

_____

_____

5 I would like to find out more about _____

_____

_____

6 This unit links with (name another unit in SPHE or another subject) _____

_____

_____

UNIT 1 Being Healthy

Learning Outcomes:

This unit helps you to:

1. Understand how your body image is linked with your self-esteem ○
2. Learn about obesity and what causes it ○
3. Understand the physical, social and psychological costs of Ireland's obesity epidemic ○
4. Appreciate the importance of feeling a sense of belonging ○
5. Discover how you can build a sense of belonging in your life. ○

(Tick off as you complete them.)

KEY WORDS

Body image
Calories
Empty calories
Obesity
Fat shaming
Sense of belonging

Diet, Physical Activity, Self-Confidence and Wellbeing

In *Health and Wellbeing: SPHE 1* you looked at the importance of healthy eating, physical activity, a regular sleep cycle and keeping yourself clean. All these elements of your life affect your self-esteem. Doing them well can contribute to making you feel worthwhile and capable. As you learned in earlier SPHE classes, your self-esteem is closely linked to your self-confidence – how much you believe in yourself.

KEY WORDS

Body image
How a person sees his or her body and how they feel about it.

It is important to understand the link between self-esteem, body image, and food and exercise.

How important is body image?

Body image has two aspects to it – how you think your body looks and how you feel about it. For example, fourteen-year-old Isabel might think that her body isn't great but she might feel fine about that because she is really good at music and that matters more to her. But fifteen-year-old Conor might think his body isn't great and he could be very upset about it. He might avoid going out and wear baggy clothes to cover himself up. Feeling negative about your body can become a vicious cycle.

Your self-esteem (how much you value yourself) and your body image (how you see and rate your body) are linked, with one affecting the other. So, the better your body image, the more comfortable you feel about how you look, and the happier you are.

Activity

1 Advertising and body image

Look at the two advertisements below, or any other advertisements you have brought into class, and answer the following questions. Your teacher will tell you if you are to work on your own or with others.

1 What messages do these advertisements give you about body image?

_____

_____

2 How accurately do these pictures represent ordinary people?

_____

_____

3 What, in your opinion, might be the results if young people saw these types of pictures on a daily basis? _____

_____

_____

Did You Know?

A series of advertisements that asked, 'Are you beach body ready?' were banned in the UK in 2016 due to concerns that they might damage people's body image.

◆◆◆◆◆◆◆◆◆◆◆◆◆
A SMILE
IS THE BEST
THING YOU
CAN WEAR
(Marilyn Monroe)
◆◆◆◆◆◆◆◆◆◆◆◆◆

A healthy diet

Having a healthy diet is an important part of being physically and mentally healthy, especially when you are still growing and developing. Last year you learned that all foods have calories and that the number of calories (kcal) per serving and per 100 grams is usually listed in the nutritional label on food packaging.

KEY WORDS

Calories

A calorie is a unit of energy. In terms of diet, calories mean energy taken in through eating and drinking and energy used up through physical activity.

Activity 2

Calorie check

 PowerPoint

We hear a lot of talk about calories. Let's see how much of it is true! Working in pairs, read the ten statements and decide if they are True or False. Your teacher will give you the answers after you have finished. Then answer the two questions below.

	Statements	True	False
1	A man, on average, needs 2,000 calories per day.		
2	People over thirty years of age need more calories per day.		
3	Heavier people need less calories than the average amount per day.		
4	The more active you are, the more calories you burn.		
5	Two slices of pizza have 1,000 calories.		
6	Carbohydrates have more calories per gram than proteins or fats.		
7	Each kilo of body fat stores 7,700 calories.		
8	If you eat 300 extra calories per day you will put on 31 pounds (14 kilograms) in a year.		
9	If you eat some foods, such as celery and cucumber, you will burn more calories than the foods provide.		
10	Texting burns 40 calories per hour.		

1 The fact about calories which most surprised me is _____

_____

because _____

2 A fact about calories that I have discovered myself is _____

_____

_____

Calories in action

Diet and physical activity are linked very simply: **Calories in – calories out!**

An example of calorie use: If you eat a medium-sized apple you would take-in around 80 calories, while a one mile walk might use up about 100 calories. So, to burn off the apple you need to walk a mile!

An average 14-year-old boy needs 2,629 calories per day, while an average 14-year-old girl needs 2,342 calories.

Activity 3

Healthy swaps

1,164 calories

890 calories

1,062 calories

A burger (508) with large French fries (444) and a large cola (212) is a chunky **1,164 calories**.

Three slices of regular crust pepperoni pizza are **890 calories**.

Fish and chips, with mushy peas makes up **1,062 calories**.

Using a calorie counter website (e.g. www.nhs.uk – lose weight, healthy food swaps section) think of two healthy, lower calorie options for your family's dinner and write them in the space below.

_____

_____

We put on wieght when we eat or drink (calories in) more energy than we use up (calories out).

KEY WORDS

Empty calories

Food and/or drinks that are high in energy but low in nutritional value, for example ice cream, sugary drinks, alcohol, cakes and biscuits.

Ireland's Obesity Crisis

How is body fat measured?

Body fat is measured using the Body Mass Index (BMI). In **adults**, this is worked out by dividing your weight in kilograms (kg) by your height in metres (m) and then dividing the answer by your height again to get your BMI.

$$BMI = \frac{Weight\ in\ kilos}{Height\ in\ metres^2}$$

Children and **teenagers** are still growing, so their BMI is worked out by comparison with national norms.

For example:

If someone weighs 60 kg and is 1.70 m tall their BMI would be:

$$BMI = \frac{60\ kg}{1.7\ m^2} = 20.76\ kg/m^2$$

$$BMI = 21$$

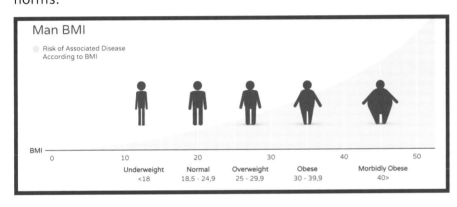

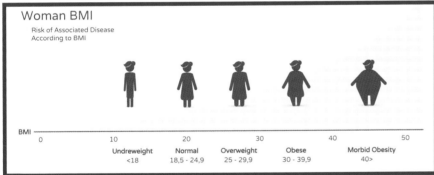

What do BMI scores mean?

The charts on the left, one for men and the other for women, show you what the different BMI scores stand for, in terms of a healthy weight for adults.

Young People and Obesity in Ireland

The Healthy Ireland 2015 survey was carried out on behalf of the Department of Health and involved face-to-face interviews with 7,539 people aged 15 and over.

The results showed that:

2% are underweight

37% are normal

37% are overweight

23% are obese

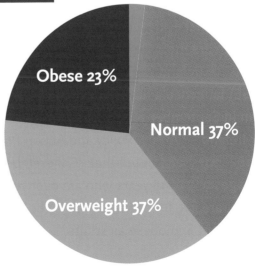

These figures mean that almost three out of every five Irish people aged fifteen and over are either overweight or obese. In the 1960s and 1970s Ireland had the thinnest population in Europe, according to Professor Donal O'Shea, Chair of the Royal College of Surgeons Ireland policy group on obesity.

At the European Congress on Obesity in 2015, a World Health Organization (WHO) report suggested that, if current trends continue, Ireland is shaping up to become the world's most obese nation by 2030.

Increasing rate of obesity in Irish adults since 1975

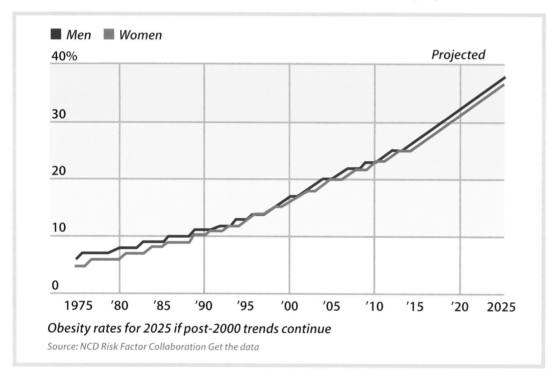

Obesity rates for 2025 if post-2000 trends continue

Source: NCD Risk Factor Collaboration Get the data

Obesity is a problem that is particularly serious for Irish young people as:

- One in four young people in Ireland are overweight or obese
- Four out of five children do not do the recommended 60 minutes of physical activity a day
- Overweight children are likely to become overweight adults
- Only 25 per cent of parents of overweight children see their children as overweight.

International evidence suggests that obese children are more likely to become obese adults. In Ireland, the Health Service Executive (HSE) launched a new national obesity action plan in September 2016, the 'Healthy Weight for Ireland – Obesity Policy and Action Plan 2016 – 2025' and noted that: 'Children between the ages of 7 to 18 years who are overweight or obese, are five times more likely to be overweight and obese as adults.'

Activity 4

Growing out of it

Imagine that you are a parent of three children – one is pre-school, one is in third class in primary school and one is in second year in post-primary school. Make a list of four simple things that you could do in your home to ensure that each child is a healthy weight.

1 Pre-school child:

_____

_____

_____

_____

2 Primary school child:

_____

_____

_____

_____

_____

_____

_____

3 Second-year student:

_____

_____

_____

_____

_____

If I were Minister for Health the first thing I would do to tackle obesity is

LEARNING LOG

What's causing the obesity epidemic?

 **PowerPoint**

Environmental factors that we can do something about are causing 99 per cent of the obesity epidemic:

Portion sizes getting bigger

Increase in people using cars, instead of walking or cycling

Availability of low-cost, high-calorie junk food

Decrease in physical activity

Advertisements and marketing campaigns aimed at young people

Easily accessible food – fast-food outlets, 24-hour shops and home freezers

Increase in people's 'screen time' – smartphones, computers and video games

tips

A **very small number** of overweight issues are caused by genes, endocrine disorders, medication and some mental illnesses. There is no reliable support or proof, however, for the theory that some people eat very little and end up gaining weight because of a 'slow metabolism'.

LEARNING LOG

The major obstacle to losing weight in my opinion is

Obesity and your health

You might be surprised to hear that obesity is the leading cause of preventable death in Ireland. According to the World Health Organization, it is also the most serious public health issue in the twenty-first century. Let's explore this further.

Activity

5

Eating your way to an early grave

Look at the list of physical and psychological health complications caused by obesity below. Draw a line between each one and the area of the body it affects.

The effects of obesity on people's health

Cancers:

- Prostate

- Breast

- Bowel

- Colon

- Oesophagus

- Kidney

- Pancreas

- Uterus

High blood pressure

Type 2 Diabetes

- Blindness

- Amputation

Hip pain

Back pain

Breathlessness

Asthma

Stroke

Gall bladder disease

Heart disease

Arthritis

Sleep apnoea

Snoring

Liver disease

Pancreatitis

Infertility

Stigmatisation

- Low self-esteem

- Bullying

- Vulnerability to depression

- Poor body image

Other costs of obesity

In the past, being fat was seen as a sign of wealth and fertility. Today obese people are more likely to suffer prejudice and discrimination. This can affect many areas of their lives, such as going for a job interview, visiting the doctor or a hospital, shopping or travelling by air.

Overweight people are often the victims of verbal abuse and ridicule – known as fat shaming. This abuse does not motivate people to lose weight. Instead it damages a person's self-esteem so that it actually makes them eat more and gain more weight.

According to research carried out in 2012 by University College Cork (UCC) for Safefood, the EU agency, the financial cost of Ireland's obesity epidemic is €1,130,000,000 (€1.13 billion). Healthcare costs are €398,000,000 and the costs of reduced productivity in Irish jobs and people being absent from work due to weight-related diseases are €728,000,000.

The money spent on obesity-related healthcare is 2.7 per cent of the entire health budget in Ireland.

KEY WORDS

Fat shaming

Criticising and making fun of overweight people about their weight, to make them feel bad about themselves.

Activity

6 Class survey

Carry out a survey using the questions below. Your teacher will give you the national results for your age group and you can compare these with yours, and any other second-year class in your school, by making a bar chart.

1. Do you eat fruit more than once a day? Yes ☐ No ☐

2. Do you eat vegetables more than once a day? Yes ☐ No ☐

3. Do you consume one or more soft drinks per day? Yes ☐ No ☐

4. Do you do vigorous physical exercise (so that you are out of breath) four or more times a week? Yes ☐ No ☐

5. Are you a member of a sports (or physical activity) club? Yes ☐ No ☐

Assessment
– Check your learning

Investigate the health value of the food, drinks and snacks available in your school or, if your school does not sell food, in the local shops. Present your findings, with suggestions for healthier options, to the student council.

Useful Websites

www.safefood.eu – search their healthy eating section for some useful tips

www.bordbia.ie – search their consumer section for a healthy eating planner

www.healthpromotion.ie – look at their suggestions on the food pyramid and eating healthy food for life

A Sense of Belonging

A sense of belonging is a core human need. It is just as important as the needs for shelter, water and food. Feeling that you belong is closely linked to feeling that you have value and meaning in your life and for helping you to deal with tough times. It is vital for the development of your IQ (intelligence quotient), your social skills and your mental and physical health.

Our earliest sense of belonging comes from our parents and close family. As you grow older, you belong to and get to know different groups – your extended family, people in your school, church and neighbourhood, acquaintances in dance and drama classes,

sports teams, clubs and so on. Many people also now belong to virtual groups such as Facebook friends, Twitter and Instagram.

Did You Know?

Research tells us that our sense of belonging can be damaged by just one case of exclusion or isolation from a group.

It is, of course, normal to feel sadness and loneliness, as these emotions are part of life. But having a strong sense of belonging helps us to handle these dark times. For example, when you lose someone close to you, your friends and relations coming to the funeral and sympathising with you can make your pain easier to bear.

Having a wide social circle may not appeal to everyone. Instead, some people are totally happy and secure feeling a connection with a small number of people. Other people may appear to belong to a wide number of groups but they struggle to find a sense of belonging. Let's explore this further.

Activity 7

What goes on in my home and community that builds a sense of belonging?

On each point of the star, write one thing that happens in your home and community to make people feel that they belong. Examples include eating together, Tidy Towns, visiting your grandparents, Meals on Wheels and so on. Then answer the questions below.

1. Discuss what you have written with two or three of your classmates and, if necessary, add any extra points to your star.

2. Draw a circle around each of the activities going on in your home or community that you are involved in.

Activity 8

What goes on in my school that builds a sense of belonging?

On each point of the star write one thing that happens in your school to make people feel they belong. Examples might be first year induction, pastoral care team, sports and uniform.

1. Discuss what you have written with two or three of your classmates and, if necessary, add extra points to your star.

2. Draw a circle around each of the activities going on in your school that you are involved in.

Take a few minutes and think about how you could build a sense of belonging in your home, community or school. Write down one thing that you could do, start or join that would improve your sense of belonging.

Build it!

Now that you have a better understanding of how to build up your sense of belonging, the good news is that it is always possible to start doing it:

- Join in
- Take baby steps at first if you are shy or nervous
- Say 'Yes', if someone invites you to do something or to be part of something (if it's not something nasty or dangerous)
- Focus on the positive. If thinking that your home is a bit messy or untidy is stopping you from inviting a friend over – don't worry about it. If you are nice and they have fun they won't care, or notice, what your home is like
- Don't make judgements; instead, focus on what's important – if you are at a party, don't whine about the food being terrible as it's the company that matters
- Watch what you say and how you say it – look at sections on tact and constructive criticism in the unit on Respectful Communications (see pages 103–109)
- Remember no one is perfect – even if they appear to be!

Remember

It's not all about you. See what you can do to give others a sense of belonging!

Activity 9

The hand of friendship

Working in groups of four, each person writes their name on one finger on the hand, along with one thing that is unique to them. This can be a simple thing like having blonde hair, a pet dog or a parent who works abroad.

In the palm of the hand, your group must write something that you all have in common. Try to find something surprising that your classmates couldn't easily guess.

Finally, on the thumb, write a name for your group.

If you want to put copies of your group's hand up on the classroom wall, trace a hand onto a sheet of paper, fill it in and use colours to make it as attractive as possible.

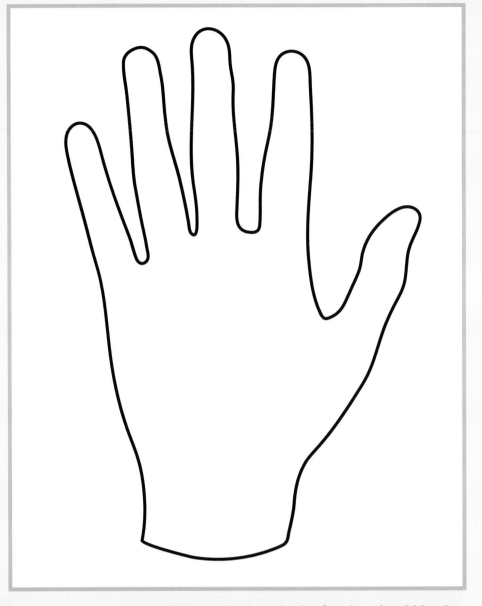

When all the groups in the class are finished, make two lists on the board. The first list should be the unique things about everyone in your class, and the second, shorter list should be the things you all have in common.

Activity 10

Class rap

Using the words on the board from Activity 9, and with the whole class working together, make a class rap. All of the words on the board must be used.

If there are other second-year SPHE classes in your school doing this topic, you could have an inter-class rap competition!

One small change I can make to help other people in my school feel like they belong is

_____

_____

_____

_____

_____

_____

Review of Unit 1: *Being Healthy*

1 In this unit I learned about _____

_____

_____

2 I think that this will help me when _____

_____

_____

3 In this unit I liked _____

_____

_____

4 In this unit I did not like _____

_____

_____

5 I would like to find out more about _____

_____

_____

6 This unit links with (name another unit in SPHE or another subject) _____

_____

_____

Minding Myself and Others

Substance Use

Learning Outcomes:

This unit helps you to:

1 Understand how the main categories of drugs work on your body and mind ○

2 Learn about cannabis and its effects ○

3 Become aware of the personal, social and legal consequences of your own and others' drug use, focusing on alcohol. ○

(Tick off as you complete them.)

In first year you learned what drugs are and what addiction means. You also had a detailed look at the most commonly used drugs in Irish society – medicines, cigarettes and alcohol. This year you will look at how drugs work and how they affect your health, relationships and society.

Let's start by checking how quickly you can do the crossword on page 83.

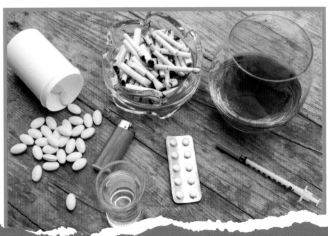

KEY WORDS

Tolerance

Withdrawal

Overdose

Physical dependency

Depressants

Stimulants

Hallucinogens

Opiates

Activity 1

Memory check!

In pairs or groups, see how much you can remember from first year by completing the crossword.

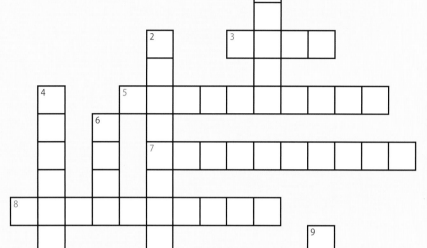

Clues across

3 A measure of alcohol. (4)

5 Drinking alcohol can lead to this. (10)

7 These contain 4,000 different chemicals. (10)

8 The use of any drug which damages some aspect of your life. (4-6)

10 These remedies are used instead of regular medicines, e.g. diets, massage and vitamin mixtures. (11)

13 Can't do without a drug. (9)

14 Medicine you can buy in supermarkets. (3)

15 A cancer linked to smoking. (4)

Clues down

1 Glues, petrol, nail polish, gas from aerosols are all types of these. (8)

2 Medicine prescribed by a doctor. (12)

4 The date after which medicine should not be used. (6)

6 Chemical which causes changes in your body. (4)

9 Having five or more alcoholic drinks in one session. (5)

11 Poison in cigarette smoke. (8)

12 One in _____ children in Ireland are negatively affected by their parents' drinking. (6)

How Drugs Work

It makes it easier to understand drugs if you know how they work and what broad categories drugs can be divided into. In first year, drug addiction was explained as when a person has no control over whether or not they use a drug and/or when their body has become so used to a drug that they have to have it to feel normal. For example, someone addicted to smoking (nicotine) could be cross and short-tempered until they have a cigarette and then they feel 'normal'.

Activity 2

Tracking the terms!

There are more terms, such as tolerance, withdrawal, overdose, addiction and physical dependency, that you need to know to help you understand how drugs work. Let's see if you know any of them already.

Each of the labels below is explained in the text on one of the five pill boxes on the right-hand side. See if you can untangle the lines and match up the correct label with its explanation. Track the trails using different coloured markers or pencils for each one.

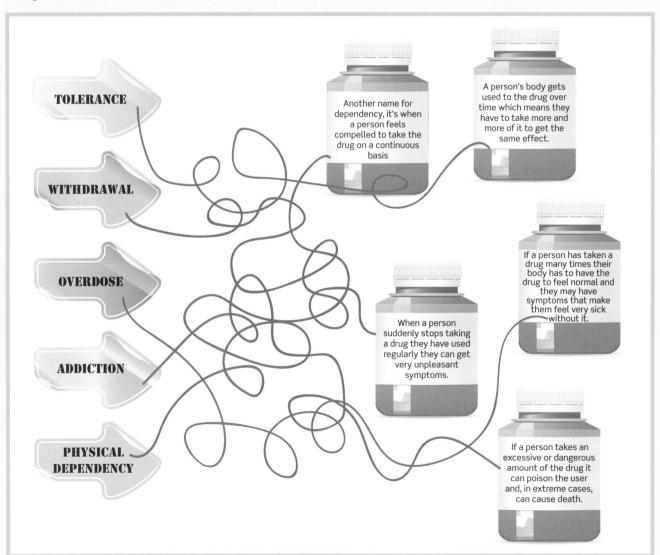

Types of drugs

Drugs can generally be divided into categories according to their effects (how they work) on people. For example, you have already learned that alcohol causes drowsiness and stupor so it comes under the category of depressants. Some drugs, such as cannabis and E (ecstasy) are listed under more than one category, as they have a number of different effects.

Categories of drugs:

1 **Depressants** 2 **Stimulants**

3 **Hallucinogens** 4 **Opiates**

KEY WORDS

Depressants
Drugs which slow down the work of your body and make you feel relaxed and drowsy.

Stimulants
Drugs which produce an increase in physical and mental activity and can 'perk you up'.

Hallucinogens
Drugs which change how you see reality – you see, hear and feel things differently, including things that do not actually exist.

Opiates
Drugs which are made from the opium poppy; sedatives that reduce pain and induce sleep.

Activity

3

 **PowerPoint**

You name it

Look at the information on the four different categories of drugs below. Read the list of each drug's effects and dangers. Then, using what you know already, draw a line to match each drug type with the names of the most common drugs from each category.

Xanax

LSD (Acid)

Sleeping pills

Alcohol

Caffeine

Methadone

Nicotine

Cannabis

Speed

Opium

Ketamine

Morphine

Cocaine

E (ecstasy)

Tranquillisers

Magic mushrooms

Valium

Codeine

Prescription painkillers

Heroin

Depressants (Sedatives)

Effects: Slow down the work of your body, making you feel relaxed and drowsy.

Dangers: Drowsiness, slurred speech, forgetfulness, overdose, convulsions

Stimulants

Effects: Increase your physical and mental activity, sometimes acting as a 'pick me up'.

Dangers: Dizziness, irritability, restlessness, panic attacks, paranoia, confusion, insomnia

Hallucinogens

Effects: Change how you see reality, so you see and hear things differently, including things that do not exist. In an altered reality, you can have feelings of euphoria (excitement, exhilaration) or nightmare visions.

Dangers: Panic attacks, restlessness, paranoia, flashbacks, imagining things, psychosis

Opiates

Effects: Often made from the opium poppy, they can be very strong painkillers and can make you to sleep.

Dangers: Overdose, dependence, health costs from the fallout from misuse (dirty needles, impure mix, etc.)

Cannabis and its effects

You probably noticed that in Activity 3 cannabis is listed under two categories: Depressants and Hallucinogens. This is because it can make people feel both depression and euphoria. These effects can depend on the strength of the cannabis, the length of time it has been stored, the amount used and the way it is used.

Cannabis is also called pot, weed, ganja, hemp, dope, grass and jungle juice. A cannabis cigarette may be called a joint, a reefer or a spliff.

Did You Know?

Just over one in four people have used cannabis, making it the most commonly used illegal drug in Ireland.

(HRB Factsheet – Cannabis: the Irish situation 2017)

Herbal cannabis

Herbal cannabis is a mix of the dried leaves and flower head of the cannabis plant. It looks like dried herbs and is smoked in a cigarette. It may be called marijuana, grass, weed or skunk.

Cannabis resin

Cannabis resin is more commonly known as hashish or hash. It is a green/brown block or slab of resin and is the most common type of cannabis found in Ireland. Hashish can be heated and smoked in a pipe or bong, or mixed with tobacco in a cigarette.

Cannabis oil

Hashish oil, more commonly called hash oil, is a thick liquid made from dissolving hashish or marijuana in solvents such as acetone, alcohol, butane or petroleum ether.

Cannabis contains over 500 different chemicals including *Tetrahydrocannabinol* (THC), which causes euphoria and CBD, which is a depressant. THC is responsible for many of the drug's psychotropic (mind-altering) effects. It's this chemical that changes a person's brain activity when they are using cannabis, distorting how their mind sees the world.

Did You Know?

Studies have found that the long-term use of THC can result in the following negative side effects:
- Short-term memory loss
- Lower mental aptitude scores
- Higher rates of psychosis and schizophrenia.

Short-term effects of using cannabis

- Increases heart rate and lowers blood pressure, increasing the risk factor for people with heart disease
- Causes short-term memory loss and interferes with learning abilities, with e.g. simple maths ability possibly affected for up to 24 hours
- Interferes with motor coordination and the ability to drive
- Causes mental/emotional effects, such as confusion and severe panic and anxiety attacks.

Long-term effects of using cannabis

If you use cannabis over a long period of time it can damage your health. The effects can include:

- Loss of memory, difficulty concentrating and being easily distracted
- Chronic bronchitis, lung damage and cancer, similar to the harmful effects of smoking (see *Health and Wellbeing: SPHE 1*)
- Possible damage to babies in the womb and after birth, as it can reach the baby through breast milk (again similar to smoking)
- Schizophrenia or depression can be triggered in vulnerable individuals, if there is a family history of mental illness
- Fertility problems in both men and women
- Dropping out of school, as research shows that young people who use cannabis regularly are more likely to abandon their studies.

Cannabis crime watch

Using cannabis can bring a young person directly or indirectly into the criminal world of drug dealers and gangland crime. This market is controlled by criminals and the money from drugs goes into their pockets.

Some interesting facts

Department of Justice

If you have a drug conviction you will be refused a visa for a number of countries, including the USA.

You could be found guilty of 'supplying' drugs even if you did not get paid for giving them to someone.

Marijuana use is positively correlated with alcohol use and cigarette use, as well as the use of illegal drugs like cocaine and methamphetamine.
(Robert L. DuPont, New York Times)

If you have a drug conviction it can be a serious problem if you need Garda clearance for state jobs, working with young people or for foreign travel/work.

It is an offence to allow your premises to be used for cultivating, supplying or smoking cannabis.

It is illegal to grow, produce, supply or possess cannabis.

Under Irish legislation if you are convicted for using cannabis you will have a criminal record.

Assessment – Check your learning

Using the information you have learned about cannabis, see if you can fill in the blanks in the text below.

Cannabis comes in three forms: _____, _____ and _____. The most common way to use cannabis is to _____ it. Cannabis does not fit into any one category of drugs as it is a sedative but can also cause _____. It has many slang names including g_____, h_____, w_____ and d_____. It has over _____ chemicals in it. Possession and supply of cannabis are _____. Memory loss and panic attacks can be _____ effects of using it and long-term effects can include an increased risk of d_____ and s_____ in vulnerable users. _____ can be affected in males and females.

One thing I learned about cannabis which surprised me was

LEARNING LOG

Alcohol: Personal, Social and Legal Consequences

No matter how little or how much alcohol people drink, their judgment is affected. It can lead people to do things that they would not normally do and often with scary consequences.

Activity 4

Free house!

In groups of four, using what you have learned about the effects of cannabis and alcohol, complete the last four frames in the storyboard below. Before you begin, spend time discussing what you want to include and planning it out. You do not need to be able to draw – stick figures are fine! The story should make it clear what risks were taken and how they affected different people. Then answer the questions below.

1. How, do you think, will the relationship between the parents and their children be affected by what happened when they were away? _____ _____ _____ _____ _____ _____ _____ _____

2. How, do you think, what happened at the party might affect the relationship between the young people and their friends? _____ _____ _____ _____ _____ _____ _____ _____ _____

Activity

5 Dangers of alcohol and drugs

Working in small groups, read the newspaper extracts on the following pages and then look at the circle on page 92. Discuss the issues covered in each article with your group and write into the circle all the effects that drinking alcohol and drug use has on the world we live in. Outside the circle, you can add in any other consequences that do not fit under the three headings.

ONESIE WEARING GALWAY MAN DRANK 18 CANS BEFORE SETTING LANDLADY'S PORCH ON FIRE

A Galway man who tried to torch his landlady's home while inebriated and wearing a onesie has been jailed. Thirty-five-year-old ███████████████████, sculled more than 18 cans of Fosters before getting into a row with his boyfriend and landlady over rent. A series of bizarre events then unfolded which culminated in the marauding, onesie-wearing drunkard, setting his landlady's, ████████████ . . . , porch on fire.

(Morgan Flanagan Creagh, www.sundayworld.com)

THEFTS AND ROBBERIES STRONGLY LINKED TO DRINK

Half of all thefts and robberies happen over the weekend and are strongly linked to drink-related behaviour, according to figures released as part of a new campaign by An Garda Síochána . . . Sergeant Alan Roughneen of the National Crime Prevention Unit said that there is a strong link between intoxication and thefts, robberies, and assaults . . . Late-night intoxication is a factor in 12% of thefts from persons, 19% of robberies and 18% of assaults.

(Joe Leogue, www.irishexaminer.com)

DRUNK DRIVER JAILED FOR SEVEN AND A HALF YEARS OVER CRASH THAT KILLED BOY (4)

Court heard ████████ consumed up to 10 pints on day of crash in ████

A drink driver who killed a four-year-old boy and severely injured his mother in a crash last year has been jailed for 7½ years . . . Judge Keenan Johnson said this victim impact statement is a wake-up call, that we as a society need to make it abundantly clear that drinking and driving is neither socially nor morally acceptable.

(Eoghan MacConnell, www.Irishtimes.com)

GARDA TELLS COURT SHE FOUND CHILD WANDERING STREET WITH HIS DRUNK MOTHER AT 5AM

A school principal said the child had complained of being hungry in school.

A District Court judge was asked to put a supervision order in place for a young boy whose mother was out drinking with him for over nine hours.

The child's social worker said the boy had missed a number of days in school and the mother could not be contacted.

(www.thejournal.ie)

PEOPLE AS YOUNG AS 20 DYING FROM ALCOHOL ABUSE

People as young as 20 have died from alcohol-related illnesses, one of the country's leading consultants has revealed.

Dr Stephen Stewart, a consultant hepatologist in the Mater Hospital, said there has been a stark increase in the number of young people who are presenting themselves in hospitals with alcohol-related illnesses in recent years.

(Emma Jane Hade, www.independent.ie)

DRUGS LINK TO 70% OF CRIMES ON PROBATION

More than 70% of crimes committed by offenders under supervision in the community were linked to drug and alcohol misuse, research shows.

The first national survey of offenders under the supervision of the Probation Service found 67% of offenders had misused illegal drugs . . .

The survey, seen by the Irish Examiner, provides a rare picture of the scale of alcohol and drug misuse among offenders and their link with crimes, such as theft, burglary, assault, and public disorder.

(Cormac O'Keeffe, www.irishexaminer.com)

23-YEAR-OLD IS JAILED FOR BURGLARIES

A 23-year-old man who admitted a number of burglaries has been jailed for 12 months.

. . . There were also a number of criminal damage and unauthorised taking of cars charges.

Defending solicitor Gerard McGovern said ██████████████ was a very unfortunate young man . . . "With alcohol he's just a fool and gets involved in this sort of thing," he said.

(www.independent.ie/regionals/sligochampion)

ASSAULTS AND DRUG ABUSE SHOW STEADY INCREASE

GARDA crime statistics for Kerry, dating back to 2004, show assaults, drug abuse and alcohol-related crime steadily increasing over a five-year period.

. . . Alcohol and drugs would appear to be the root cause of much of the problem with substance abuse related crimes, assaults, drink driving, theft and burglary, drug possession or dealing and general vandalism all moving steadily upwards.

(Simon Brouder, www.independent.ie/regionals/kerryman)

PERSONAL   **SOCIAL**

Drugs and
Alcohol

LEGAL

1 Check what the other groups in your class came up with and add any extra points into your circle.

2 What are the consequences of alcohol and drug abuse that you think apply especially to young people?

_____

_____

_____

_____

_____

_____

_____

3 What, do you think, can be done to reduce the damage caused by the misuse of alcohol and drugs?

_____

_____

_____

_____

_____

_____

_____

Assessment – Check your learning

Choose one of the areas of risk from the circle in Activity 5 and make a poster highlighting the dangers in that area. Your poster should be as powerful as possible and include the contact details of any agencies that help people affected by drug and alcohol problems. Keep it in your SPHE folder or e-folder.

Useful Websites

www.easyread.drugabuse.gov – search for information on the effects of using drugs

www.kidshealth.org – in Teens search Drugs and Alcohol for good, easy to understand information on tobacco, alcohol (including parents drinking) and a range of other drugs

Review of Unit 2: *Substance Use*

1 In this unit I learned about _____

_____

_____

2 I think that this will help me when _____

_____

_____

3 In this unit I liked _____

_____

_____

4 In this unit I did not like _____

_____

_____

5 I would like to find out more about _____

_____

_____

6 This unit links with (name another unit in SPHE or another subject) _____

_____

_____

Minding Myself and Others

UNIT 3 Respectful Communication

Learning Outcomes:

This unit helps you to:

1 Learn more about assertive communication ○

2 Practise appropriate assertive communication ○

3 Become aware of sensitive and respectful communication ○

4 Understand how to give – and take – constructive criticism. ○

(Tick off as you complete them.)

KEY WORDS

Assertiveness

Sensitive communication

Tact

Appropriate communication

Criticism

Constructive criticism

KEY WORDS

Assertiveness

A positive way of communicating where you are able to speak up for yourself in a respectful and truthful way.

The Importance of Assertiveness

Communication, or getting your message across, is about much more than the words you say. Last year you learned about how people communicate, the importance of body language and how your tone of voice and emphasis affects what

you say. You also found out about listening skills, how to be a good listener and the three different communication styles – passive, aggressive and assertive.

Let's take a closer look at assertiveness.

Activity 1

Being assertive

Read the statements below describing how to be assertive. In the empty clouds, write three extra life skills that you think are examples of what it means to be assertive.

Giving a compliment

Making a complaint

Asking for help

Saying you're sorry

Being able to disagree respectfully

Expressing your feelings in a suitable way

Feeling comfortable accepting a compliment

Being able to say 'No'

Being comfortable with difference

Standing up for yourself

How assertive are you?

There are eleven statements below about different aspects of assertive behaviour. Read each sentence and rate yourself from 1–4 on how good you are with each skill: **1 is very poor; 2 is poor; 3 is good; and 4 is very good**.

If you find it hard to be assertive with some people or groups of people write their names into the third column. For example, you might be able to say 'no' to your family but not to your friends, so you would write in 'friends' or if you can usually ask for help at home but not at school, write school in the third column.

	Assertiveness skills	Score	People/Groups I find it difficult to be assertive with:
1	Giving a compliment		
2	Accepting a compliment		
3	Saying 'no'		
4	Expressing my feelings		
5	Saying I'm sorry		
6	Being comfortable with difference		
7	Asking for explanations		
8	Making a complaint		
9	Disagreeing respectfully		
10	Asking for help		
11	Standing up for myself		
	Overall Score:		

Add up the numbers in the score column to get your total.

Less than 15: You need to work on your assertiveness skills or people might take advantage of you. Pick one or two areas, for example asking for help or giving compliments, and start with these. When you get more confident with these skills you can move on to working on two other skills and so on.

16–27: You are a little bit assertive, but you have work to do in some areas and with some people.

28–37: You seem to be fairly assertive. Check your answers. Are there some skills that you scored well on? Can you figure out why these are better than others? Which assertiveness skills do you need to work on?

38–44: Well done! You know how to be assertive but it's important that you pay particular attention to the section on appropriate assertive communication on page 99. You need to make sure that you are aware of how other people are reacting when you are being assertive.

In pairs or groups, compare your results and discuss the questions below:

1. Do you find it harder to be assertive with some people than others? If so, why is this?

2. Are there some assertiveness skills that the class in general are better at than others? If so, what are they?

Advantages of assertive communication

There are many advantages to being able to communicate assertively:

- It helps you to feel good about yourself and others
- It makes life simpler because other people do not have to guess what you want
- It increases your self-esteem
- It helps you to achieve your goals
- You are less likely to hurt people
- It reduces your anxiety as you don't keep things bottled up
- It protects you from being taken advantage of (used) by others.

Disadvantages of assertive communication

Sometimes there are disadvantages to communicating assertively:

- Some people do not like this style of communication or may not approve of the views you express
- People can sometimes feel that young people should be 'seen and not heard' and should not be assertive
- In Irish society people might think that expressing yourself assertively is rude
- Being aware of other people's rights means you won't always get what you want and you may have to change your viewpoint on something.

Tips for being assertive

 **PowerPoint**

- Use your body language to show that you are confident – take a deep breath, stand up straight, look people in the eye and relax.
- Speak in a firm but pleasant tone.
- Don't expect the other person to be awkward – be positive!
- Know exactly what you want to say and say it clearly. Rehearse it beforehand if you need to.
- Use the 'broken record' technique – repeat and repeat and repeat your message – until you believe that you have been heard.
- Don't forget to listen and ask questions as it's important to understand the other person's point of view as well.
- Pick a time when neither you or the other person is rushing and when you are both fairly calm.
- Never make personal or insulting comments.
- Try to think 'win–win' in any situation and find a compromise so that, if possible, both persons' needs are met.

From what I have learned about assertive communication the part I find the hardest is

One thing I can do about this is

Appropriate Assertive Communication

Assertive communication is open and honest and helps people to get on and live together in an uncomplicated way, but there are times when it might not be the best type of communication to use. You have to be aware of other people's needs and how they may be feeling. For example, if someone is upset and crying, straight talking is unlikely to be the thing that they need at that time.

To make sure that you don't make the other person feel bad you may need to change the way you communicate with them. Sometimes you need to take a minute to think about what might be going on in the other person's life – the 'context' of the situation – before you say something you might regret to them.

KEY WORDS

Appropriate communication
Communication that is fitting or suitable for the occasion.

Did You Know?

There are huge cultural differences in the meaning of gestures. For example, the thumbs-up sign usually means 'well done' or 'OK' here but in Iran, Afghanistan, Nigeria, South America and the Middle East it is an obscene insult similar to holding a middle finger up.

Look up more of these yourself!

Activity

3   Reading the clues

 Animation

On the following pages are four different scenarios that will help you to understand the idea of 'Appropriate communication'. Read each of the scenarios, 1–4, and then decide whether each of the given responses is an example of assertive communication, aggressive communication or passive communication. Then circle the response you think is the most appropriate thing to say in the circumstances and explain why you think so.

Scenario 1

A friend of your parents is visiting your house for the first time and he comes into the sitting room where you are watching *The Simpsons* on TV. He picks up the remote and switches channels so that he can watch the 'News at 6'. What is the best thing to do?

	Response	Communication style
A	You say, 'Hey baldy, I was watching *The Simpsons*. Turn it back!'	
B	You quietly pick up your mobile and look at something on it.	
C	You calmly say, 'Excuse me, would you mind turning back to *The Simpsons* please?'	

1 The most appropriate response in this situation is (A/B/C) _____ because _____
_____

2 Write a response that you think would be better than the three given above.

_____
_____

Scenario 2

Your friend's parents have taken you out for dinner. The extremely busy waiter has brought your chips but forgotten the tomato ketchup. What is the best thing to do?

	Response	Communication style
A	You eat them anyway.	
B	You try to catch the waiter's eye and quietly ask for ketchup.	
C	You shout in the direction of the waiter, 'Excuse me, could you bring me the ketchup please?'	

1 The most appropriate response in this situation is (A/B/C) _____ because _____

_____

_____

2 Write a response that you think would be better than the three given above.

_____

_____

Scenario 3

You are meeting a friend at the cinema. You buy the tickets and wait. And wait. Thirty minutes later your friend arrives. She explains that on the way to the cinema her dad's car had a flat tyre and it took ages to fix it. What do you say?

	Response	Communication style
A	I've been standing here for thirty minutes! Why didn't you text?	
B	It doesn't matter, I didn't mind waiting.	
C	Oh, forget it! You're always late anyway!	

1 The most appropriate response in this situation is (A/B/C) _____ because _____

_____

_____

2 Write a response that you think would be better than the three given above.

_____

_____

_____

Scenario 4

You are standing on the bus on the way home when you feel somebody's hand taking your mobile phone from your pocket. What do you say?

	Response	Communication style
A	You shout at the top of your voice: 'Hey! Take your hand out of my pocket, you thief!'	
B	You say quietly but firmly: 'Do you mind taking your hand out of my pocket please?'	
C	You whisper: 'You can have it, I have another one at home.'	

1 The most appropriate response in this situation is (A/B/C) _____ because _____

_____

_____

2 Write a response that you think would be better than the three given above.

_____

_____

Reading the Situation

Part of growing up and becoming more adult is learning how to 'read' situations. This means knowing what type of communication style is the most suitable one to use for different situations. For example, if you are under attack or in danger, your natural response might be aggression and to use aggressive communication.

In a different type of situation, while it is important to be assertive, good manners sometimes mean that you must be passive in how you react to events. For example, if your Gran keeps asking you the same questions and telling you the same stories, it would be rude to tell her that it's really irritating you, or if someone is upset or ill it may also not be a good time to use assertive communication.

Your relationships with the person can also make a difference. For example, you can get away with using a level of assertiveness with your family that might not be suitable for your dealings with someone you have just met, visitors or those in authority, such as one of your teachers or the school principal!

Activity 4

Trouble in school

It is between classes and your class is in uproar. Lots of students are out of their desks, talking and messing around. You are quietly sharpening your pencil at the bin inside the door. Your teacher storms in and you are the first student she sees. She says: 'You again! You are always out of your seat. Give me your journal; I'm going to put a note in it and you need to get a parent to sign it!'

You tell her that you are only coming from the bin but she says she could hear you as she came down the corridor. What do you say?

Response A   'That's not fair! You're always picking on me.'

Response B   'Sorry Miss,' and hand her your journal and plan to talk to her at the end of the class when it is calmer.

Response C   'Miss you couldn't have heard me. I wasn't talking. I was coming from the bin.'

1 Which response is passive? _____

2 Which response is assertive? _____

3 Which response is aggressive? _____

4 Why did you choose the response you did? _____

_____

Assessment – Check your learning

Three groups prepare a two-minute role play for each response, A, B and C, in Activity 4. These are performed for the class. Remember what you have already learned about facial expressions, posture, tone of voice, emphasis and gestures. Begin with the teacher entering the room.

While watching the role plays take notes in your copybooks and have a class discussion about the following questions when the role plays are finished:

1 Do the actors stay in character (aggressive, passive or assertive) for the whole role play?

2 Which approach has the best outcome? Why do you think this is?

> **Keep to your SPHE 'Class Ground Rules' during the role plays. Do not say or do anything to hurt other people in your class.**

Sensitive and Respectful Communication

Let's have a closer look at the importance of being sensitive to others when we are listening and talking to them. It's important to learn how to give and hear opinions in a way that respects the other person's feelings.

If someone asks you something and your honest answer would be harsh or hurtful it would be better if you could find a tactful way to respond so that you are sensitive to their feelings but you don't lie. For example, if your mum

asks you if you like her new dress and you think it's hideous, you could always put a positive twist on it by saying that the colour is great on her, that the length really suits her or that it's not as good on her as her red dress.

KEY WORDS

Sensitive communication

Being aware of the attitudes, feelings and circumstances of others in our dealings with them.

KEY WORDS

Tact

A keen sense of what to say or do to avoid giving offence to other people; skill in dealing with difficult situations and people.

5 Truth or tact

Read the scenarios 1–4 below and think about what you would do if you found yourself in a similar position. Your teacher will tell you whether to do this on your own or in a group. Then decide what you would do or say, after thinking about the following:

- Is this a difficult situation for you? Why is this?
- How would you feel if you were the person in the scenario?
- How would you like to be treated?
- Has anyone ever been insensitive or tactless with you? What did it feel like?

Scenario 1: The debating team

Every year a team from the second-year classes takes part in a debating competition. Lots of students, Gavin included, hope to get a place on the debating team. However, he is quietly spoken, stumbles over his words and it's often really hard to hear him. He doesn't make the team and he is disappointed and angry. He thinks the teacher only picked her favourites. Gavin asks your opinion.

What do you say?

_____

_____

Scenario 2: The new girl

You and your friend have known each other since Junior Infants. You are now at the same post-primary school and are still close friends. However, one of the new girls insists on hanging around with the two of you and you find this very annoying. She doesn't seem to know anyone else in the class. You wish she would leave you and your friend alone.

What do you do or say?

_____

_____

Scenario 3: The wallpapered bedroom

You have just returned from holiday to find your mother has redecorated your bedroom without consulting you. You think, 'This is the bedroom from Hell! No way can I bring my friends here!' Your mother is delighted with the new wallpaper and asks you what you think.

What do you say?

Scenario 4: The dating dilemma

Your friend Jan fancies one of the boys, Alex, who gets the same school bus as her. He seems to have no interest in her at all, even though she texts him all the time, tries to sit near him on the bus and wants to go out with him. Jan doesn't really look after herself. She has a problem with body odour and her hair is often greasy. Jan asks you what you think her chances are with Alex.

What do you say?

Tact tips

Before responding to something ask yourself the following:

- What might be the effect of what I do or say on other people?
- How might I feel?
- How might they feel?
- Is it worth taking the risk?

THINK

BEFORE YOU SPEAK

T is it TRUE?

H is it HELPFUL?

I is it INSPIRING?

N is it NECESSARY?

K is it KIND?

I learned that being tactful is important because

_____

_____

One area of my life where I could be more sensitive is

_____

_____

One change I need to make that will help me be more tactful is

_____

_____

Criticism

Most of us don't like it when we are criticised. We think criticism is only about making negative remarks or comments about somebody's faults or problems with doing something. But this only applies to negative criticism and people sometimes use this type of criticism to put you down.

Constructive criticism, however, is a good thing. People can use it to make positive remarks or comments to help you.

How constructive criticism works

Constructive criticism or advice is useful and is intended to help or improve something. The critic (the person giving the criticism) can help you by suggesting possible solutions.

There are two main ingredients of constructive criticism:

1   It is given to help you.

2   It includes suggestions about how you might improve.

An example of constructive criticism would be if your teacher explains to you that your essay is too short and that you could improve it by having an introduction, a conclusion and four paragraphs, each on a different topic.

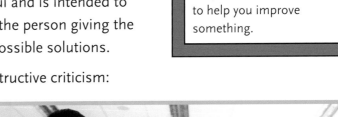

KEY WORDS

Criticism
The act of passing judgments on someone or something.

KEY WORDS

Constructive criticism
Helpful and useful advice to help you improve something.

Activity 6 | Flipping it!

Your teacher will tell you, or your group, which situation from the four below to work on. Read it and change the negative criticism to constructive criticism. Remember, your comments must include suggestions for improving the issue. Then answer the questions.

1 Your mother has gone to a lot of trouble to make a new recipe for lamb balti. It tastes awful and you struggle to eat it.

Negative criticism: This dinner is disgusting – the dog wouldn't eat it!

Constructive criticism:
_____
_____
_____
_____
_____
_____

2 Your friend Pia has had a disagreement with Anna, another girl in your class. Pia was very nasty to Anna. She now expects you to agree that she was right and that Anna was wrong.

Negative criticism: No Pia, you were a total witch to her.

Constructive criticism:
_____
_____
_____
_____
_____

3 Your boyfriend/girlfriend swears a lot and sometimes you find it very embarrassing. Otherwise you like him/her very much.

Negative criticism: You really need to look at the amount of swearing you do – it's mortifying.

Constructive criticism:
_____
_____
_____
_____
_____
_____

4 Your friend Zac has got a new hairstyle that he loves but it does not suit him. It looks stupid and the colours are vile. Zac paid a lot of money for it and he asks you if you like it.

Negative criticism: Honestly, you look like someone electrocuted your head!

Constructive criticism:
_____
_____
_____
_____
_____
_____

1 Discuss your answers with other people in your class who looked at the same situation. Would you change any of your answers after listening to their constructive criticism? _____

2 If so, what changes would you make and why?
_____
_____

3 What are the risks in giving constructive criticism?
_____
_____

The constructive criticism sandwich

A good way of giving someone constructive criticism is to sandwich it between positive comments. This way the person should not feel hurt or belittled. You should use three layers in your criticism sandwich – *compliment*, *criticism* and *compliment*. For example, if your friend makes a mean comment you might say, 'I think you're the funniest person in our class but not everyone shares your sense of humour and sometimes you go a bit too far. Your good friends know that you are only messing!'

Here you are telling your friend that he is really funny (*compliment*), that he can sometimes upset people (*criticism*) and that he has good friends (*compliment*).

Let's look at a second example. Your friend Lisa asks what you thought of her performance in the football game which your team lost. You say, 'You were really fast (*compliment*) but you held on to the ball too long (*criticism*), which I can't understand because normally you're a team player (*compliment*).

Assessment – Check your learning

Role play

Your teacher will divide you into groups and assign one of the four situations described in Activity 6 to each group. Write a role play for it, using the constructive criticism sandwich method. The three layers – compliment, criticism, compliment – do not need to be given in the same sentence or speech.

While students from each group are performing their role play for the class, look at the questions below and, in your copybook, write a report on each situation.

1 How sensitive (caring, kind) was the critic, the person giving the criticism?

2 How did he/she show this?

3 How well did the other person take the criticism?

4 What could have been done differently?

One thing I learned in this lesson about how I give or take criticism is

LEARNING LOG

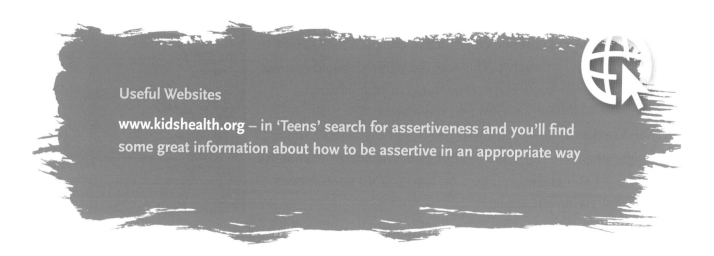

Useful Websites

www.kidshealth.org – in 'Teens' search for assertiveness and you'll find some great information about how to be assertive in an appropriate way

Review of Unit 3: *Respectful Communication*

1 In this unit I learned about _____

_____

_____

2 I think that this will help me when _____

_____

_____

3 In this unit I liked _____

_____

_____

4 In this unit I did not like _____

_____

_____

5 I would like to find out more about _____

_____

_____

6 This unit links with (name another unit in SPHE or another subject) _____

_____

_____

Minding Myself and Others

Learning Outcomes:

This unit helps you to:

1 Understand the difference between teasing or 'slagging' someone and bullying them ○

2 Learn how your school's Internet Safety – Acceptable Use Policy protects everyone in your school community from bullying ○

3 Become aware of the serious effects of all types of bullying, including cyberbullying, on someone's mental and physical health, self-esteem, sense of belonging and happiness, and that of their friends and families. ○

(Tick off as you complete them.)

In *Health and Wellbeing: SPHE 1* you examined exactly what 'Bullying' means and looked at the different types of bullying. You learned how to deal with bullying and the important role that bystanders can play in helping to end bullying.

Let's have a quick look back at what you learned.

KEY WORDS

Anti-Bullying Policy

Internet Safety – Acceptable Use Policy

Code of conduct

Victim Impact Statement

Bullying Mind Map

In first year you learned a lot about bullying. Here is a recap of some of the most important information.

Relational bullying involves isolating, excluding, ignoring or spreading rumours about someone.

The main types of bullying are cyberbullying, extortion, relational bullying, name calling, physical, intimidation, identity-based bullying and damaging property.

Bullying has physical, emotional and social effects.

If you are being bullied, avoiding the situation or ignoring the behaviour can help you to deal with it.

If you are bullied or if you see bullying taking place, you should always TELL someone.

All schools have an Anti-Bullying Policy.

Cyberbullying is using information technology (IT), like mobiles, laptops or tablets, to post hurtful information about someone online or to send nasty emails, texts or messages to them on social media websites like Facebook, or to upload embarrassing or damaging photos of them.

People who see someone being bullied or know bullying is going on are called bystanders.

Activity 1 — Fill in the blanks

Using the information in the mind map, and in *Health and Wellbeing: SPHE 1*, fill in the blanks below. All of the words are supplied in the 'Word Bank' but see how many you can get without using it!

Bullying is _____, unwanted, negative behaviour. Fighting, hitting, spitting and punching are all part of _____ bullying. Anybody can be a bully or a _____. Bullying someone by breaking their mobile phone, pencil case, books or schoolbag comes under _____ _____. Targeting people because they have special educational needs, are a different colour, race or religion, are disabled, LGBT or a member of the travelling community is called _____ bullying. Relational bullying is very common, especially amongst _____. It means isolating, _____ or making fun of someone.

_____ is becoming increasingly common as most young people now have their own _____ _____ or tablet. While bullying is generally repeated behaviour, a _____ _____ offensive, hurtful or nasty text or online message, photo, like or share on a social network site, or other public medium e.g. mobile phones, is seen as bullying as it can possibly be seen, copied or forwarded by thousands of people. Every single device (smart phones, tablets, computers) that is connected to the Internet has its very own _____ _____ which can be used to track all messages sent from it.

Some of the best ways of dealing with bullying are to ignore it, give no _____, _____ places and situations where the bullying usually happens and to tell an _____ that you trust.

Word Bank

IP address, reaction, Cyberbullying, identity-based, avoid, ignoring, physical, mobile phone, damaging property, repeated, one off, victim, girls, adult

Only joking?

Many people make jokes and funny comments to their friends, family and other people online and in person. Joking, teasing or 'slagging off' someone is seen as a bit of fun. Sometimes, however, this type of joking can cross the line from harmless to hurtful and can become bullying.

Activity 2

Crossing the line

In pairs or groups, write down three 'Harmless' things people say or do and then write three 'Hurtful' things that people say or do that you think 'cross the line'.

1 What are the signs that someone doesn't think something is funny?

_____

_____

_____

2 What do you think it feels like to be in that situation?

_____

_____

_____

Harmless

_____
_____
_____
_____
_____
_____

Hurtful

_____
_____
_____

Who draws the line?

You do!

If someone is 'slagging' or teasing you and you do not like what is posted or you think the joke has gone too far then it doesn't matter if everyone else thinks that the texts/posts/photos/comments are hilarious. It's what you, the victim, thinks that counts.

Remember

If you don't like what someone is saying or doing to you it's important that you let them know – if it's safe to do so.

School policies and anti-bullying

Last year you looked at your school's Anti-Bullying Policy and how it could help you if you were being bullied. Your school's Internet Safety – Acceptable Use Policy deals with cyberbullying.

KEY WORDS

Internet Safety – Acceptable Use Policy

Outlines how all aspects of the Internet are to be used by students and staff so that students can use this technology to learn in a safe way.

You should know what these policies say because, as a student in the school, your behaviour has to follow these rules. Most schools have posted these policies on the school website.

Activity

3 The court case

Read the information below and hold a mock trial in your classroom to decide if some of the terms in your school's Anti-Bullying Policy and Internet Safety – Acceptable Use Policy were broken.

To do this you will need a copy of your school's:

- Anti-Bullying Policy
- Internet Safety – Acceptable Use Policy
- Code of Conduct (or Code of Discipline).

You can see examples of the relevant sections of these policies below but it would be better if you use your own school's policies to do this activity.

KEY WORDS

Code of Conduct

Also called the 'School Rules' or 'Code of Discipline', it outlines what is acceptable and unacceptable behaviour for students and what the rewards are for good behaviour and what the sanctions (punishments) are if you breach (break) the rules.

CHARGE: Breaching your school's Anti-Bullying Policy and your school's Internet Safety – Acceptable Use Policy.

Carraiglen College basketball team have a WhatsApp group called Carraiglen All Stars. There are ten students in the squad but only eight are in the WhatsApp group. One player, Tom Foyle, and his friend, another player, Dean Kiefelt, do not know about it. Tom is popular in school, gets top marks in his subjects and is usually good at games, but he hasn't been doing that well in the last few matches.

Some of the team members in the group have been commenting on Tom's playing. Instead of Foyle, they call him 'Fool'. A friend of one of the WhatsApp group, Student X, saw the texts and told Mr Moylan, the teacher who coaches the team, about them.

EVIDENCE:

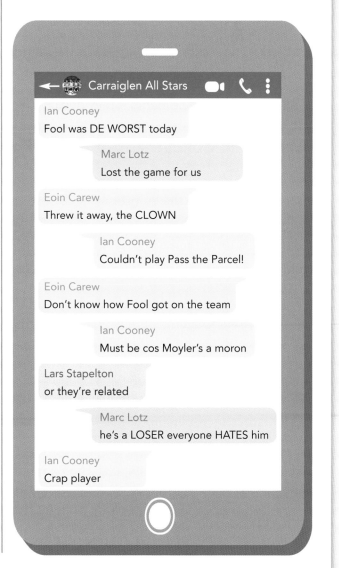

Carraiglen All Stars

Ian Cooney
Fool was DE WORST today

Marc Lotz
Lost the game for us

Eoin Carew
Threw it away, the CLOWN

Ian Cooney
Couldn't play Pass the Parcel!

Eoin Carew
Don't know how Fool got on the team

Ian Cooney
Must be cos Moyler's a moron

Lars Stapelton
or they're related

Marc Lotz
he's a LOSER everyone HATES him

Ian Cooney
Crap player

In the mock trial you need to find out:

1 Is any of this behaviour against the school's Anti-Bullying Policy?

2 After reviewing the Internet Safety – Acceptable Use Policy, did the WhatsApp group break any of the school rules?

3 If the answer to either of the above questions is 'yes', use the Code of Conduct to decide what a fitting sanction would be.

> **Remember**
>
> It is the effect of the bullying on the victim that's important. Saying it was just a laugh makes no difference.

You need students to take the following roles:

Judges: Three, with one being the Chief Judge – if the jury find that the defendants are guilty of any of the charges the three judges decide on the sanctions, if any.

Prosecution barrister(s): One or two – present(s) the case for the prosecution.

Defence barrister(s): One or two – present(s) the case for the four defendants.

Defendants: Ian, Marc, Eoin and Lars – the four students posting messages on the WhatsApp group.

Bystanders: The four other boys who were on the team and part of the WhatsApp group but not part of this particular chat.

Witnesses: Tom Foyle, Dean Kiefelt, Mr Moylan, Student X (not named to protect his identify) – they tell their side of the story.

Court Clerk: One – calls each witness to the stand.

Jury Foreperson: Head of the jury.

Jury: All the remaining students – they decide whether or not any rules have been broken.

Carraiglen College Anti-Bullying Policy (excerpt)

Definition

In accordance with the 'Anti-Bullying Procedures for Primary and Post-Primary Schools', bullying is defined as follows:

'Bullying is unwanted negative behaviour, verbal, psychological or physical conducted by an individual or group against another person (or persons) and which is repeated over time.'

The following types of bullying behaviour are included in the definition of bullying:

- Deliberate exclusion, malicious gossip and other forms of relational bullying
- Cyberbullying – a form of harassment using text messages, e-mails and websites to bully someone
- Identity-based bullying such as homophobic bullying, racist bullying, bullying based on the person's membership of the Travelling community and bullying of those with disabilities or additional/special educational needs.

Isolated or one-off incidents, including a one-off offensive or hurtful text message or other private messaging do not fall within the definition of bullying and should be dealt with, as appropriate, in accordance with the Carraiglen College's Code of Behaviour. However, in the context of this policy, placing a one-off offensive or hurtful message, image or statement on a social network site or other public forum where that message, image or statement can be viewed and/or repeated by other people will be regarded as bullying behaviour.

Sanctions

Bullying will not be tolerated. Where bullying takes place, sanctions may include any one, or a combination of, sanctions listed in the School's Code of Behaviour.

Carraiglen College Internet Safety – Acceptable Use Policy *(excerpt)*

Students will treat others with respect at all times and will not undertake any actions that may bring the school into disrepute.

Students will not send or receive any material that is illegal, obscene and/or defamatory, or that is intended to annoy or intimidate another person.

Students who leave a mobile phone turned on or use it in class, to send nuisance text messages while in school or to take unauthorized still or moving images with a mobile phone camera, are in direct breach of the school's Internet Safety – Acceptable Use Policy.

Cyberbullying is defined as a form of harassment using text messages, e-mails and websites to bully someone. Any incident of cyberbullying involving students, as either perpetrator or victim, is a concern, but especially when both perpetrator and victim are students.

If the school's Internet Safety – Acceptable Use Policy is not adhered to, it may result in disciplinary action in line with the school's Code of Behaviour. The school also reserves the right to report any illegal activities to the appropriate authorities.

Only use the excerpts given here if you can't get copies of your school's policies.

Carraiglen College Code of Behaviour *(excerpt)*

Sanctions

- Verbal reprimands
- Teacher note in student journal
- Written warning – copy sent to parents and copy placed in student's file
- School community tasks – cleaning, picking up rubbish, tidying the library etc.
- Detention
- Referral to the Dean of Discipline
- Student placed On Report
- Loss of privileges; attendance at matches, out of school events, etc.
- A Contract of Behaviour may be introduced
- Where the student has brought the good name of the school into disrepute the student may be removed from positions of privilege within the school such as membership of the Student Council, position as a Class Prefect, membership of school teams, etc.
- In serious instances of misbehaviour, a student may be suspended in accordance with the Carraiglen College Suspension and Expulsion Policy.
- In the case of serious recurring behaviour or an incident of gross misbehaviour, a student may be expelled in accordance with the Carraiglen College Suspension and Expulsion Policy.

The Trial

Arrange your classroom so that it looks like a courtroom. Have areas for the judges and the prosecution and defence teams. The jury, witnesses and defendants sit in their own groups. At the start of the case the Court Clerk tells everyone what the charge is and what school policies may have been breached (broken).

Court Clerk: All rise for the judges.

(Judges take their seats)

The Court Clerk reads out the charges:

Court Clerk: The four defendants stand accused of breaching the school's Anti-Bullying Policy and Internet Safety – Acceptable Use Policy.

Court Clerk: I call on the Prosecution to *briefly* introduce their case.

Prosecution: State what they are going to prove to the jury – two or three sentences stating the parts of the school's policies which the defendants have breached.

> Your teacher will give you extra information if you need help here.

Court Clerk: I call on the Defence to *briefly* introduce their case.

Defence: State what they are going to prove to the jury – two or three sentences stating how the defendants did not breach any school policies, and talking about any special circumstances which might lessen their guilt.

Court Clerk: I call the first witness for the Prosecution: _____

All the witnesses on the Prosecution's list are called. The prosecution barrister questions them first; then the Defence can ask them questions. Witnesses would probably be Tom Foyle, Dean Kiefelt, Mr Moylan and Student X. They might consider calling a bystander, one of the other four players who were part of the WhatsApp group but who were not involved in these particular texts.

Court Clerk: I call the first witness for the Defence: _____.

All the witnesses on the Defence's lists are called. The Defence barrister questions them first; then the Prosecution can ask them any questions. Witnesses would probably be the four defendants, and then perhaps character witnesses to say that the defendants are usually well-behaved students. The Defence also might consider calling a bystander, one of the other four players who were part of the WhatsApp group but who were not involved in these particular texts.

Court Clerk: I call on the Prosecution to give their summary.

Prosecution: The prosecution team *briefly* summarise their case.

Court Clerk: I call on the Defence to give their summary.

Defence: The defence team *briefly* summarise their case.

Chief Judge: The chief judge gives instruction to the jury, reminding them of the parts of the three school policies which are relevant to this case.

The jury withdraws to consider their verdict.

(The jury can go to a corner of the room to do this.)

While this is happening, the judges can look at the list of sanctions in the Code of Behaviour and decide on one, or more, that they will apply if the defendants are found guilty.

At the same time, Tom, Dean and Mr Moylan can prepare their Victim Impact Statement, stating what effect the behaviour of the defendants has had on them – in terms of their self-esteem, their happiness in school, their enjoyment of basketball, their families, their study, their sleep patterns, their health (physical and mental) and so on.

The jury returns and the jury foreperson gives a page to the Chief Judge.

On this sheet is written:

- The parts of the Anti-Bullying Policy, if any, each defendant breached.
- The parts of the Internet Safety – Acceptable Use Policy, if any, each defendant breached.

Chief Judge: Reads out the jury's verdict.

Victims: The victims, Tom, Dean and Mr Moylan, read separate, or joint, Victim Impact Statements.

Chief Judge: Thanks the jury and then comments on the case in general and tells the court what sanctions (if any) the judges have decided on.

> **KEY WORDS**
>
> **Victim Impact Statement**
>
> A statement that the victim gives to the court, before sentence is passed, about the effect the crime has had on them and their life.

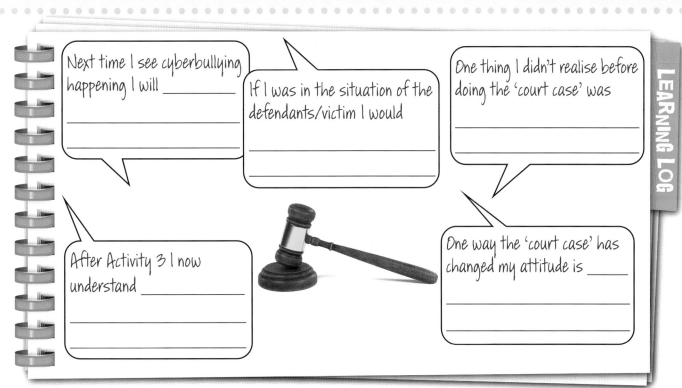

LEARNING LOG

Next time I see cyberbullying happening I will _____ _____ _____

If I was in the situation of the defendants/victim I would _____ _____

One thing I didn't realise before doing the 'court case' was _____ _____

After Activity 3 I now understand _____ _____ _____

One way the 'court case' has changed my attitude is _____ _____ _____

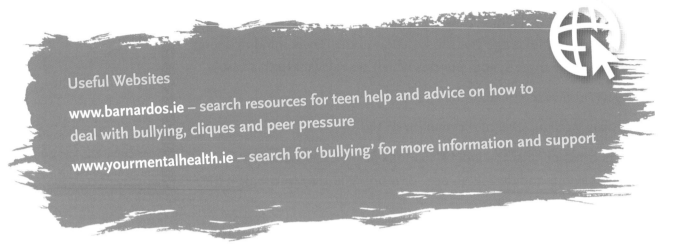

Useful Websites

www.barnardos.ie – search resources for teen help and advice on how to deal with bullying, cliques and peer pressure

www.yourmentalhealth.ie – search for 'bullying' for more information and support

Review of Unit 4: *Anti-Bullying*

1 In this unit I learned about _____

_____

_____

2 I think that this will help me when _____

_____

_____

3 In this unit I liked _____

_____

_____

4 In this unit I did not like _____

_____

_____

5 I would like to find out more about _____

_____

_____

6 This unit links with (name another unit in SPHE or another subject) _____

_____

_____

UNIT 1 Having a Friend and Being a Friend

Learning Outcomes:

This unit helps you to:

1. Understand that your friendships can change throughout your life ○
2. Think about what type of friend you are to others ○
3. Learn how to handle difficulties in your friendships. ○

(Tick off as you complete them.)

Changes in Your Friendships

By now you will have experienced many different kinds of friendship and you will appreciate that having friends is important to you for many reasons. Friendships can be complicated and at this stage in your life they can change a lot. This is a normal and natural part of growing up.

In the activities in this unit you will explore how friendships change and identify what is important to you in your friendships.

KEY WORDS

Friendship
Value
Friendship qualities

KEY WORDS

Friendship
Having a friend or friends.

Why do friendships change?

Friendships can change for a number of reasons. You or your friend might move to live in a different place or change schools. Maybe you no longer have interests or hobbies in common and you just grow apart. Changes like these are part of life, and being able to deal with them and learn from them is an important part of growing up.

Keeping friendships going takes time and effort. For many people, the friends you make as a teenager will be special because they are there for you during the ups and downs of adolescence, at a time when it may be difficult for you to talk about your worries and troubles.

Activity

1

How your friendships have changed

Take a few moments to think back to when you were in *second class* in primary school and the friends you had then. Look at the circles below and write your name in the centre. In the next circle write the names of your closest friends in second class.

In the middle circle write the names of your more casual friends. Maybe you'd sit with them at lunch or walk home from school with them. In the outer circle write the names of acquaintances, people you didn't really think of as friends but who you talked to now and again. Instead of writing their names, you could use a symbol, drawing or initial to represent them.

When you have completed the 'second class friendships' circle, think about the friends you have now in second year. Fill in their names in the friendship circle for second year and then answer the questions.

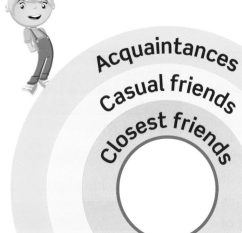

Second class friendships   **Second year friendships**

My friends in second class and second year

1 Are there some friends you were once closer to than you are now? If so, why?

_____

_____

2 Are you still friendly with them even if you are not close friends?

_____

3 Are there other people you are now closer to? Why do you think this is so?

_____

_____

4 Do you have friends now who you didn't have before? How did you make friends with them?

_____

_____

5 Are your close friends living near you or far away? Does this matter?

_____

_____

6 Are you closer or less close to your brothers and sisters than in the past? Why?

_____

_____

LEARNING LOG

I think that my friendships have changed since I was in second class because

_____

The friends I'm closest to now are my friends because

_____

Three things I can do to be a good friend are:

1 _____

2 _____

3 _____

Friendships – changing values

Now that you have explored some reasons why friendships change you may realise that this can sometimes happen because what you value in the friendship is no longer the same as what your friend values. Let's look at what qualities you value in your friends and why you value these qualities.

KEY WORDS

Value

Something you cherish and believe is important to you and guides your behaviour.

123

Activity

2

What do you value in a friendship?

Read the list of qualities that young people sometimes value in a friendship below. On your own, rank them from 1 to 10, in order of what you think is important. Give a brief reason as to why this quality is important to you. Rate the most important quality you want in a friend as 1 and the least important quality as 10.

Quality	Rating	Reason
Rich		
Kind		
Generous		
Fun-loving		
Intelligent		
Similar interests		
Good-looking		
Loyal		
Friends in common		
Have a positive outlook		

Activity

3

Diamond 9

KEY WORDS

Friendship qualities
The characteristics of a friendship.

In groups of four, discuss your rankings and agree on a group ranking of the qualities you all value in a friend (this might be difficult if you value different things in a friendship!). You must agree on nine qualities and rank them from 1 to 9, with 1 being the most valued quality and 9 being the least valued. This means that **you must agree to drop one quality**.

If there is a quality that's not on the list that your group thinks is important, then decide on a second quality you'd like to omit and include the new one.

In the Diamond 9 on the next page write in the qualities your group have agreed on. Number 1 will be the quality in a friend that you agree to be the most important. Then you will have two second priorities, three third priorities, two fourth priorities and one that you agree is least important.

Then complete the Learning Log.

Diamond 9

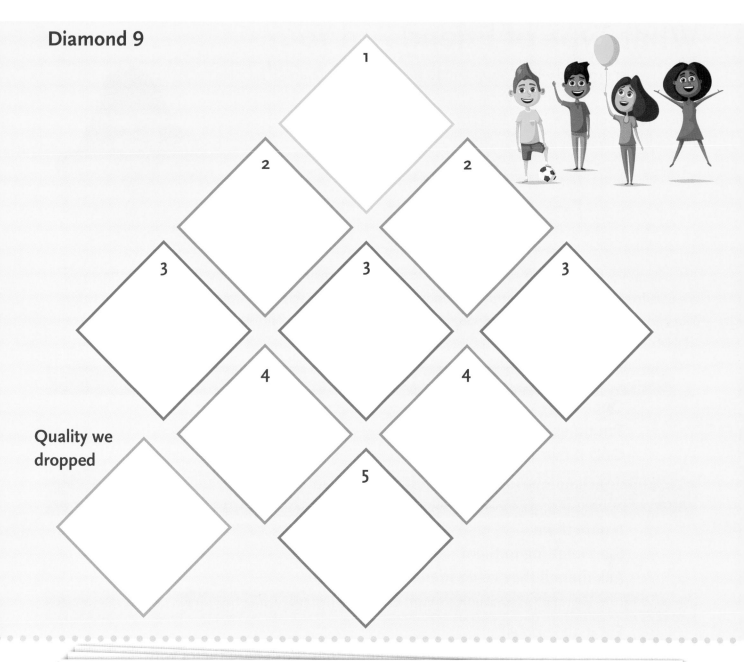

1

2   2

3   3   3

Quality we
dropped   4   4

5

The quality that my group agree is most important in a friendship is

because

The quality we had difficulty agreeing on was   because

My idea of what's important in a friendship changed during Activity 3 because I

Something I learned about myself as a friend from Activity 3 is

LEARNING LOG

What Type of Friend Are You?

You have just explored what's important to you in a friendship. Before you find out more about the challenges of dealing with difficulties in your friendships let's see what kind of friend you are – a BEST friend or a PEST friend.

Activity

4 — Friendship quiz

This is a quick fun quiz and **you don't have to share your results with anyone**. Think about how you are as a friend and for each of the questions tick which of the three answers, a, b or c, applies to you. Then add up your scores and rate yourself, using the scale at the end, to find out whether you are a BEST friend or a PEST friend.

1 How often do you message your best friend?

(a)	Once a day	☐
(b)	Ten times a day or more	☐
(c)	Only if I've something to say	☐

2 You are talking to your best friend and someone else comes along. What do you do?

(a)	Ignore them	☐
(b)	Start chatting to them	☐
(c)	Ask them if they've no friends of their own	☐

3 You have a bar of chocolate as part of your lunch. What do you do?

(a)	Eat it all yourself	☐
(b)	Share it with your friend on condition that they share theirs with you next time	☐
(c)	Eat some yourself and from time to time offer a piece to your friend	☐

So how did you do?

10 – 15: Best friend – you are considerate, kind and respectful, and willing to give your friend some space

7 – 10: Some room for improvement – you can be a bit inconsiderate at times

3 – 7: A lot of room for improvement – you can be quite rude and a bit selfish, both with your best friend and with others

Remember, keeping in touch with your friend is important but texting non-stop for no reason might show that you don't trust them or that you feel insecure in your friendship.

1 (a) = 5
  (b) = 1
  (c) = 3
2 (a) = 3
  (b) = 5
  (c) = 1
3 (a) = 3
  (b) = 1
  (c) = 5

Friendship Problems – When Things Don't Work Out

You will know by now that having friends and being a true friend is an important part of your life as a teenager. For your friendships to survive the test of time and all the ups and downs in your life there needs to be give and take on both sides. But this can be difficult at times.

Being honest and open with your friends about how you feel when problems come up is an important ingredient in a healthy friendship. It can make your friendships stronger because you know where you stand with one another. However, everyone grows and changes over the years and friends can change too. Sometimes this can bring friendships to an end.

Activity 5 — Friendships – what can go wrong?

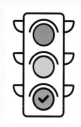

Let's look at some statements about your friend that might be warning signs that your friendship is at risk. As your teacher reads out each one, hold up your red, green or orange traffic light page at the back of your book to show what you think – choose red if you think the statement is a warning sign, green if you think it's a healthy aspect of a friendship or orange if you are unsure. Mark in your answers below.

Statements – Your friend:	Agree	Disagree	Unsure
	Green	Red	Orange
1 Allows you to be yourself.			
2 Makes too many demands on your time.			
3 Resents you having other friends.			
4 Supports you when you are in difficulty.			
5 Checks up on you when you are sick.			
6 Criticises you.			
7 Gets into a huff with you and doesn't explain why.			
8 Spreads rumours about you.			
9 Encourages you to try new things.			
10 Doesn't share your interests.			
11 Talks honestly about your friendship, even when things are not going well.			
12 Regularly cancels arrangements without explaining why.			
13 Accepts you as you are.			
14 Gets jealous when you do well.			
15 Trusts you with their innermost secrets.			
16 Always replies to your texts immediately.			

Select three statements – one that you disagreed with (red traffic light); one that you agreed with (green traffic light); and one that you were unsure about (orange traffic light) – and explain why you made each decision.

Disagreed

Statement number ___

Reason: _____

Agreed

Statement number ___

Reason: _____

Unsure

Statement number ___

Reason: _____

Healthy and unhealthy friendships and relationships

As soon as you are born you begin to form relationships with your parents, brothers, sisters and family. As you grow up, your friends and friendships become even more important to you. However, sometimes it may be necessary to end a friendship or relationship as it might not be in your best interest. For example, if you realise you can no longer trust your friend or that they are making demands on you that make you feel uncomfortable. Maybe you need to avoid

unhealthy friendships/relationships like the examples above – but sometimes it can be difficult to tell the difference between a healthy friendship/relationship and an unhealthy one.

Activity 6 Healthy or unhealthy – what's the difference?

In groups of four, brainstorm the characteristics of either a healthy friendship/relationship or an unhealthy one. Your teacher will tell your group which type to do. Write the characteristics under the appropriate heading on page 129.

Share your list with the class and then, as all the groups read their lists out, write in any extra characteristics your group did not include. Do this for both healthy and unhealthy friendships/relationships. Then complete the Learning Log.

**Healthy
friendships/relationships**

**Unhealthy
friendships/relationships**

Think about a friendship you enjoy now and one which didn't work out and ended for one reason or another. Why was it that one friendship ended and the other didn't? Then complete the sentences below, using the lists of characteristics from **Activity 6** to help you.

In a healthy friendship, I feel

In an unhealthy friendship, I feel

Sometimes it is difficult to end an unhealthy friendship because

LEARNING LOG

What can you do if there is a problem?

Being aware of a problem between you and your friends is one thing but being able to do something about it is something else. It can be difficult to know what is the best approach. Do you try to talk to your friends and fix the problem or do you have to face the fact that your friendship/relationship is over? This is a very hard thing to do as losing friends or breaking up a relationship can make you feel hurt and worried. Let's look at some tough situations and see how you might handle them to deal with the problem.

7

When the going gets tough

In groups of three, read the scenarios below and answer the questions on one of the scenarios, A–F. Your teacher will tell you which one to discuss. Think about whether or not the people involved really want the friendship to end or what else might work.

Scenario A – Joanna and Maeve

Joanna and Maeve started first year on the same day. Neither of them knew anyone else in the class so they became good friends quickly. Now they are in second year and Maeve is ignoring Joanna. She seems to have become really friendly with Vicky over the summer. Joanna is hurt and doesn't know what to do.

1 How might Joanna and Maeve feel?

_____

2 What could Maeve say or do?

_____

3 What could Joanna say or do?

_____

4 What would be a good way to deal with this problem?

_____

Why? _____

5 What would be a bad way to deal with this problem?

_____

Why? _____

Scenario B – Susan and Adam

Susan and Adam are in second year and have been friends since fourth class in primary school. Their school was running a poster competition with the title 'Dealing with Tough Times' and Susan decided to enter as she is good at art. Susan was excited about the competition and shared her ideas with Adam. Adam entered as well and won the competition but it seems that he stole Susan's ideas. They aren't really talking to one another now.

1 How might Susan and Adam feel?

_____

2 What could Susan say or do?

_____

3 What could Adam say or do?

_____

4 What would be a good way to deal with this problem?

_____

Why? _____

5 What would be a bad way to deal with this problem?

_____

Why? _____

Scenario C – Jack and Milo

Jack and Milo love football and they have played for the same club for two years. Now that they are in second year they both really want to get on the school team. They are training like mad for this and are competing with one another all the time. After training on Tuesday afternoon, the team coach asks Jack to play on the school team the next day. Jack is really fired up and can't wait to play. Milo wasn't at training and he hears about this through someone else.

1 How might Jack and Milo feel?

_____

2 What could Jack say or do?

_____

3 What could Milo say or do?

_____

4 What would be a good way to deal with this problem?

_____

Why? _____

5 What would be a bad way to deal with this problem?

_____

Why? _____

Scenarios D, E and F – what would you do?

Scenario D – Rumours

You discover that your friend has been spreading rumours about you that are not true. She's been sending texts to a WhatsApp group she set up without telling you.

1 How might you feel?

_____

2 What could you say or do?

_____

3 What would be a good way to deal with this problem?

_____

Why? _____

4 What would be a bad way to deal with this problem?

_____

Why? _____

Scenario E – Fallout

You have two very close friends who have recently fallen out with one another. You feel very uncomfortable as they both expect you to take their side in the row and keep sending you texts and messaging about it. You want to stay friends with both of them.

1 How might you feel? _____

_____

2 What could you say or do? _____

_____

3 What would be a good way to deal with this problem? _____

_____

Why? _____

_____

4 What would be a bad way to deal with this problem? _____

_____

Why? _____

_____

Scenario F – Under pressure

Your best friend starts acting in a way that you are not happy with and feel is wrong – smoking, skipping classes and so on. You sometimes feel under pressure to join in but you aren't comfortable doing any of it.

1 How might you feel? _____

_____

2 What could you say or do? _____

_____

3 What would be a good way to deal with this problem? _____

Why? _____

_____

4 What would be a bad way to deal with this problem? _____

Why? _____

_____

Now that I have thought about how I am as a friend and what qualities I value in my friends, I think I am a good friend because

I can be a better friend by

I GET BY
with a little help
FROM MY FRIENDS

– John Lennon

Assessment – Check your learning

In pairs, make up a short role play to illustrate ways of ending a friendship. Write a script for either of the situations below and include what each person might say. Remember what you learned about body language and non-verbal communication in first year and include notes on this in your script. Then act out the role play for the rest of the class.

Option 1
Ending a friendship in a way that is respectful and not hurtful to the other person.

OR

Option 2
Ending a friendship in a way that is uncaring and disrespectful of the other person.

Useful Websites

www.kidshealth.org – the teen health section is a great source of information, support and advice if you have questions about your friendships

www.barnardos.ie – information on loads of issues relating to young people and has a Q and A section on teenage friendships

Review of Unit 1: *Having a Friend and Being a Friend*

1 In this unit I learned about _____

_____

_____

2 I think that this will help me when _____

_____

_____

3 In this unit I liked _____

_____

_____

4 In this unit I did not like _____

_____

_____

5 I would like to find out more about _____

_____

_____

6 This unit links with (name another unit in SPHE or another subject) _____

_____

_____

UNIT 2 The Relationship Spectrum

Learning Outcomes:

This unit helps you to:

1. Understand the different relationships in your life ○
2. Appreciate that all families have similarities and differences ○
3. Discuss ways of starting a relationship ○
4. Learn about respecting yourself and others in different kinds of relationships ○
5. Explore the importance of having boundaries in relationships and setting your own personal boundaries. ○

(Tick these off as you complete them.)

KEY WORDS

Relationship
Family
Blended family
Respect
Personal boundaries

Relationships in Your Life

Relationships are about the connection between two or more people. How people feel and behave towards one another are important elements of any relationship.

For most people, your first relationship is with your family. What you learn from this relationship and how people in your family treat one another often influences your friendships and relationships as you grow up. The attitudes and values you learn from being part of your family often shape who you will be as an adult.

KEY WORDS

Relationship

Way in which people are connected.

Family

A group of people who are related to each other and/or who have a shared commitment to one another.

If you look around your school and neighbourhood you will see that there are many different kinds of families. Each family is unique and different and because of this you are unique and different too.

Families – all the same and all different

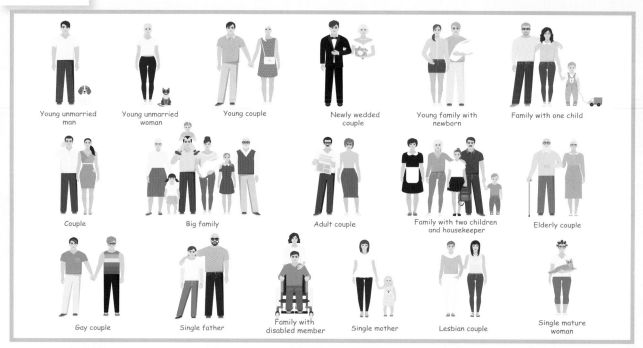

Look at the ten statements about families below. After reading each statement, tick the relevant box if you agree, disagree or are unsure.

Do this activity on your own first. Then when your teacher reads out each statement you can show your response by holding up one of the red, green or orange 'Traffic Lights' pages at the end of your textbook. You will find out how other people in your class think. You may think quite differently about some of the statements and that is good too.

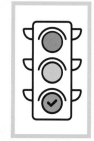

Then, in groups of three, discuss your answers and in the space below, write one sentence that explains what family means to you.

Statements		Agree	Disagree	Unsure
		Green	Red	Orange
1	Families live together.			
2	Family members should stick up for each other.			
3	All families have secrets.			
4	Parents/guardians are always right.			
5	Family members love each other.			
6	A person only has one mum.			
7	To be a family a couple must have children.			
8	All families are different.			
9	Happy families never argue.			
10	All parents/guardians have favourites.			

To me a family is _____

_____

_____

KEY WORDS

Blended family

Made up of a couple, the children they have had together and their children from previous relationships.

Family influence

Living with any group will shape and influence you, whether it's your birth family, step family, adoptive family, blended family or a family headed by your grandparents. We see our parents and care-givers as role models and we learn from them. In the activity below you will explore some of the ways in which your particular family influences, or has influenced, you.

Activity 2

The 'This is me' collage

Remember your SPHE 'Class Ground Rules' and be sensitive about other people's collages.

Make a collage, on a sheet of A4 paper and keep it in your SPHE folder, on this page, or digitally and save it to your e-folder. **Use words, pictures, symbols or drawings to show the range of influences that have contributed to making you the teenager you are today.**

Think about what you look like, what kind of personality you have, your hobbies and interests, how your family and friendships have shaped you and how your culture might have influenced you.

With three classmates, share as much of your collage as you feel comfortable discussing. See how similar and different influences have shaped you and the other people in your group.

What has shaped me?

Looking at your collage, identify two influences that you value and appreciate. Then identify two which maybe you'd prefer to leave behind as you get older.

Two influences I value are

Two influences I'd prefer to move on from as I grow up are

Managing Relationships

You will know by now that your friendships and relationships can, and do, change over time. You have thought about the different attitudes and values that are important to you in your friendships.

As you get older you will form new and more complex relationships. Making new friends and establishing new relationships can be exciting but it can also be a difficult time for people, as you need to think about what behaviour is acceptable and what is not. Let's explore some of the relationships that a second-year student might have.

Beginning a relationship

You have already looked at the range of relationships you have in your life – with your parents/guardians, brothers and sisters, neighbours, classmates, close friends and other friends through social media and so on. Over the next few years you may have a new type of relationship as you start going out with your first boyfriend or girlfriend.

There is no set time for you to start having a boyfriend or girlfriend. You may feel that you are ready now but your parents/guardian may have different ideas about this depending on your family background (including your culture and religion), your values, how mature you are and so on. Many people don't have a boyfriend or girlfriend until they have finished school because they are involved in other things that are more important to them and they are happy with that.

3

Danny's dilemma

 Animation

Read about Danny's dilemma below and discuss the questions with two others. Then write in your answers.

Danny's life

Most of Danny's friends meet up every month to hang out and listen to music. One or two of his friends have a boyfriend or girlfriend but Danny has no

Danny

Age: 14

Family: Mum, two younger brothers and two younger sisters

Hobbies: Football, listening to music, skateboarding and reading

Close friends: Lucy and Paul

real interest in going out with someone at the moment. He goes along for the fun anyway because he doesn't want to feel left out. Last month some of Danny's friends started to slag him because he wasn't with someone. They were joking around and told some of the girls that Danny fancied them. Now he sees some of them pointing at him and laughing. Danny feels uncomfortable as he has no interest in having a girlfriend right now. Up to this he has been happy but now he feels under pressure. He can't talk to his parents or his Mum and sisters as he would be way too embarrassed. He's not sure what to do.

1. Why, do you think, are Danny's friends acting this way?

   _____

2. How, do you think, Danny might feel?

   _____

3. How might this pressure affect Danny?

   _____

4. What would you advise Danny to do?

   _____

   _____

5. Do you think young people are under pressure to be in a relationship? If so, why?

   _____

6. Do you think boys and girls have similar expectations about what will happen when they are in a relationship? Why is this?

   _____

7. What other concerns do you think Danny might have?

   _____

   _____

Remember

Everyone is different and every couple in a relationship is different too. There is no set time for someone to start having a boyfriend or girlfriend. Do what feels comfortable for you and move at your own pace. Don't feel pressurised by anyone.

Activity

4

Breaking the ice

Being in a relationship can be exciting but sometimes knowing how to start a new relationship is difficult as it's hard to think of anything to say. Let's see how you could tackle this. Look at the images below and write in what you think the other person might say if he/she wanted to 'chat somebody up'.

Activity

5

'Interview' questions

To find out more about how to start a relationship, come up with a list of questions to ask someone you'd like to go out with. Think about the qualities you'd like the other person to have and what sort of person you'd like them to be.

In groups of four, come up with a list of four questions and combine these with questions from another group. See what questions you have in common and which ones are different. If you like a question from another group, add it to your group's list.

Going out with someone should be fun.

In your group, rank your four favourite questions in order from 1 to 4, with 1 being the most important question you want to ask. Then write them on page 141.

As each group reads out their four questions, see how your group's rankings compares with each list. If you are in a mixed class find out if there are similarities between the questions asked by boys and the ones asked by girls.

1 Our group's four favourite questions are:

1 _____

2 _____

3 _____

4 _____

2 Two questions I think are important are:

1 _____

because _____

2 _____

because _____

3 A question I didn't think of but which is important to me is _____

because _____

4 Two differences between what boys might ask and what girls might ask are:

1 _____

2 _____

LEARNING LOG

For me the most important factor in whether or not to have a boyfriend or girlfriend is

_____

Two qualities that are important to me in a relationship are

_____

Two qualities I'd bring to a relationship are

_____

Respecting Myself and Others

As you go through your life, you meet a range of people with whom you have different types and levels of relationship. For example, you have a much closer relationship with your family and friends than with your teachers or your doctor. So, with each of these different relationships, you often behave in a different way. For example, you wouldn't discuss a row that you had with your mother with your swimming coach but you might do so with a close friend. How you behave in a relationship says something about how much you respect yourself and others. Let's explore this a bit more.

KEY WORDS

Respect

Having consideration for the feelings, wishes and rights of others.

Activity 6

Julie's day

It's another busy day in the Daly household and Julie is already a bit behind. She has breakfast with her family – her dad, her sister, her stepmother and her stepbrother. Leaving the house in a rush, Julie has to sprint to catch the bus. The bus driver waits for her and she flops down beside her best friend, Fred, whom she has known since second class in primary school. There's nothing that Julie wouldn't share with Fred.

It's a busy morning ahead but Julie doesn't mind as they have a half day today in celebration of the school winning a second Green Flag. Despite this some teachers seem hassled, including Julie's Aunt Claire who teaches Julie Maths. The only fun Julie has that morning is at break with her friends Pat and Faye and at soccer practice, even though her coach is grumpy too!

After school Julie has a dental appointment to have her teeth checked and her night brace readjusted.

She gets home, quickly changes and rushes to the local newsagent to buy a card for her grandmother's birthday. She dives into McCoy's post office to buy stamps and post the card. Then she heads for the bus stop. It's busy so Julie gets in the queue and bumps into Jackie McCoy, who used to be one of her best friends in primary school. Julie feels awkward as they drifted apart after they went to different post-primary schools and they have nothing in common any more. She's really relieved when the bus comes!

She just makes it to her 4.00 p.m. piano lesson with Mr Wilson, a friend of Julie's mum. Julie used to look forward to her weekly lesson but things have changed and she's not as enthusiastic any more. In fact, Julie is beginning to dread going to her piano class but she hasn't been able to tell her mum this.

After tea Julie gets her bag packed for her scout hike next morning. Fred's dad is scout leader. Then at 7.30 p.m. she calls over to her boyfriend Owen's house and chats to his mum while she's waiting for him to come back from soccer practice.

Owen and Julie have been going out together for four weeks now and they often go to the cinema on Friday nights. Owen is Julie's first boyfriend and she feels comfortable and safe when she is with him.

1 Read Julie's story again and think about the different sorts of relationships that Julie has with the people she met throughout the day. They are divided into five different categories:

- Family: People closest to Julie – her dad, stepmother, boyfriend
- Friends: Close friends and relatives
- Casual friends: Other friends and acquaintances, classmates
- Professionals: Neighbours, professional people Julie has contact with
- Strangers: People Julie doesn't know at all.

Circle the relationships in the story using different colours: green for family; yellow for friends; blue for casual friends; red for professionals; and grey for strangers.

Write the relationships into the correct column in the table below, placing the person that Julie is closest to highest up on the list. For example, Fred is Julie's best friend so he will be top of the list in the 'Friends' column. You can put the same person in more than one category.

Family	Friends	Casual friends	Professionals	Strangers

2 Which relationships were easiest to categorise? Why?

_____

_____

3 Which were the most difficult to categorise? Why?

_____

_____

4 Did you place any people in more than one category? Why?

_____

_____

5 Why do you think Julie sees Fred as her best friend?

_____

_____

6 Are there any categories that should never overlap? Why/why not?

_____

_____

Activity 7

Julie's Facebook page

Read what Julie posted on her Facebook page about her day and, in groups of three, come up with some advice to help her. Try to be specific in saying what actions you think Julie can take. One person from each group then reads out their advice. Write your answers to the questions in the space below.

Julie

Was really looking forward to half day today! Soccer was cool, got picked for the U14 team... all that practice paid off!! Feeling good didn't last long – love piano but I'm dreading the lessons. Mr Wilson is creepy. He keeps moving his chair closer and touching my leg. The smell of smoke off his breath makes me sick! Today he stood behind me and leaned right down over me, pointing out the notes. I HATE it and I'm freaking about going again next week. I can't tell my mum as Mrs Wilson's one of her best friends. Anyway, she'd probably tell Dad and he'd say I'm causing trouble and ground me for the weekend. Then I wouldn't see Owen. Couldn't stand that... drama central! What'll I do? Help!

Advice to Julie

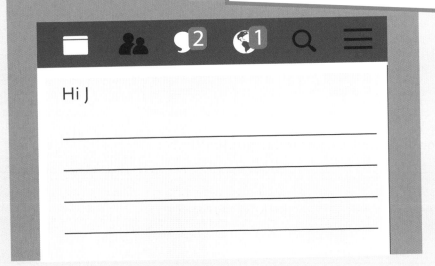

Hi J

1. Why, do you think, does Julie say that Mr Wilson is creepy?

2. Why is she asking for help?

3. How, do you think, does Julie feel?

4. What might stop Julie telling someone how she feels about what's going on?

5 What might help Julie so she can tell someone what's going on?

_____

_____

6 If you were Julie's friend, how could you support her?

_____

_____

7 From listening to what other students advise Julie to do and thinking about your group's advice, what would you encourage Julie to do now?

_____

_____

Personal Space and Boundaries

 PowerPoint

Julie felt very uncomfortable when Mr Wilson was moving his chair closer to her, touching her leg and leaning in over her. He was invading her personal space and crossing an invisible line – her personal boundary. Your personal boundary helps you decide what kind of behaviour or communication you will accept from others. Someone crosses your personal boundary if they stand too close to you and you feel uncomfortable, or if they touch you in an inappropriate way. Setting your own personal boundaries helps you to keep physically and emotionally healthy.

KEY WORDS

Personal boundaries

The guidelines, rules or limits that each person creates to protect them from being used or abused by others.

If someone crosses the line:

- Say NO – use your assertiveness skills
- Walk away or run to a safe place
- Tell someone you trust – a parent/guardian, older brother or sister, teacher or counsellor.

Did You Know?

In a recent study of over 8,000 people from 42 countries researchers found that Argentinians have the smallest personal space boundary, keeping a distance of 76 cm from strangers, while, at 1.3 m, Romanians have the largest. (_Journal of Cross-Cultural Psychology_)

Keeping your personal boundaries safe

In Activity 7 it was clear that Julie related to people in her life on different levels, from her mum and her boyfriend Owen, with whom Julie was very close, to Mr Wilson, who was being creepy because he was invading her personal space and touching her in ways that made her feel uncomfortable.

As you grow older, it's important that you know how to take responsibility for maintaining healthy boundaries and that you learn some rules for keeping yourself safe when these boundaries are crossed.

Setting and keeping healthy boundaries take practice. Here are some tips that might help you.

- Recognise how you are feeling – are you uncomfortable, stressed or worried?

- Acknowledge that your boundary has been crossed.

- Don't be afraid to tell the other person that you are not happy with the situation.

- Be assertive and direct by using 'I' statements to tell the other person how you feel and that your boundary has been crossed.

- Think about what you want and how to say it.

- Don't be concerned about how the other person will feel or react.

- Look after yourself, talk to someone you trust and ask for help.

Activity 8

Is this behaviour acceptable?

This activity will help you to explore the ideas of personal space, boundaries and appropriate touching in more detail.

1 Look back at the table in Activity 7 and at the people you placed in the different levels of relationships in Julie's life. Place these in the appropriate circles in the diagram.

2 From the 'List of behaviours', choose what you think is acceptable behaviour for the different people in each of the relationship levels. Write that behaviour (e.g. shaking hands) beside each person's name in the circles. For example, Fred – giving a high five.

5 Strangers
4 Professionals
3 Casual friends
2 Friends
1 Family

3 Some of these behaviours are never acceptable. Write any behaviour that you think is unacceptable in the space below.

_____

_____

List of behaviours

Shaking hands, hugging, rough and tumble, slapping, holding hands, kissing, pinching, touching private parts of the body, kicking, being forced to touch someone else, standing so close to someone that it feels uncomfortable, biting, patting gently on the shoulder, cuddling, looking into another person's eyes, giving a 'high five', nodding hello to someone, paying no attention to someone at all.

Activity

9 Watch your personal space – crossing boundaries

Now that you have thought about what behaviours are acceptable and appropriate for the different people in Julie's life, think about the people in your life and about the behaviour you feel comfortable accepting from them. Think about the people you know and about your personal space and the kind of touching that is acceptable or unacceptable to you. Work out why you feel this way. For example, you might be prepared to accept hugs from close family members but not from a neighbour.

With two other students, come up with three ideas about how to deal with a situation where your personal boundaries are crossed. For example, if someone touches you inappropriately. Write them in the space below.

Situation:

_____

How to deal with it:

_____

_____

_____

_____

_____

_____

Remember

In the 'Stay Safe' programme in primary school you learned about what is acceptable and what is unacceptable in terms of touching and physical contact.

LEARNING LOG

Having personal boundaries is important to me because

Something I can do to keep myself safe and ensure that my personal boundaries are not crossed is

If someone crosses these boundaries I know I can get help from

Sometimes it is hard to ask for help because

Assessment – Check your learning

You will see notices about the Child Protection Policy in your school. This is to ensure that your school is a safe place for everyone. It also tells you what you can do and who you can go to if you have concerns about your own personal safety or the safety of another student.

Find out the answers to the three questions below about your school's policy.

STAY SAFE

1 Who can you talk to in your school if you have a concern?

2 Who is the Designated Liaison Person (DLP) in your school?

3 What can you expect the DLP to do for you?

If you are worried about your own safety or anyone else's safety it is important that you talk to a trusted adult who can help you. Think about someone you could go to if you need help.

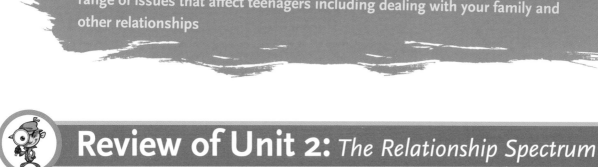

Useful Websites

http://kidshealth.org – find information on healthy relationships and knowing your own mind in the teen health section

www.childline.ie – search their support section for useful information on a range of issues that affect teenagers including dealing with your family and other relationships

Review of Unit 2: *The Relationship Spectrum*

1 In this unit I learned about _____

_____

_____

2 I think that this will help me when _____

_____

_____

3 In this unit I liked _____

_____

_____

4 In this unit I did not like _____

_____

_____

5 I would like to find out more about _____

_____

_____

6 This unit links with (name another unit in SPHE or another subject) _____

_____

_____

Team Up

UNIT 3 Sexuality, Gender Identity and Sexual Health

Learning Outcomes:

This unit helps you to:

1 Revise the parts of the male and female reproductive systems ⭘

2 Learn about fertility, conception, prenatal development and birth ⭘

3 Appreciate how important it is for the mother to look after her health during pregnancy ⭘

4 Explore some personal and social dimensions of sexual orientation ⭘

5 Identify ways in which your school is an inclusive one, particularly for students who are LGBT (lesbian, gay, bisexual and transgender). ⭘

(Tick these off as you complete them.)

From Conception to Birth

Between conception and death, human beings experience three periods of rapid growth and change:

1 From conception to birth
2 The first year of life
3 Puberty

Last year you learned about the changes that take place in your body, your mind and in the rest of your life during puberty. You also explored in detail the physical changes that take place inside and outside your body. Some of these changes mean that you are physically able to become a parent.

This year, you will look at how a baby develops from the time of its conception to its birth. Before exploring this process let's see what you can remember from first year about the parts of the male and female reproductive systems.

> **KEY WORDS**
>
> **Conception**
>
> The act of becoming pregnant – when the egg from the female is fertilised by the sperm from the male.

> **KEY WORDS**
>
> Conception
> **Reproductive system**
> Pregnancy
> Embryo
> **Foetus**
> Birth
> Placenta
> Sexual orientation
> Inclusive school

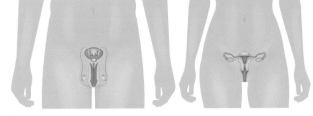

Male and female reproductive systems

Activity 1

What do you remember?

Using words from the list below, label the different parts of the male and female reproductive systems in the diagrams.

cervix   sperm ducts   testes   ovaries   scrotum   urethra
vagina   penis   uterus (womb)   fallopian tubes

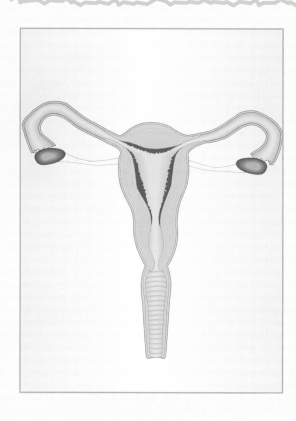

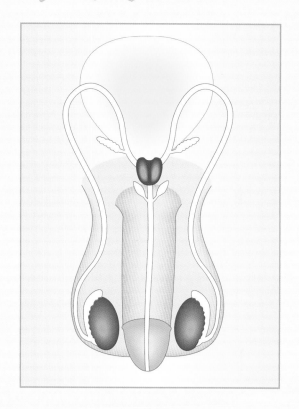

Let's look in more detail at what happens from conception to birth.

How does pregnancy begin?

In first year, you learned that if fertilisation does not take place during a woman's menstrual cycle, the egg from the ovary dies. It leaves the woman's body, along with the lining of her womb, as part of her period. However, if the couple have had sex and the woman's egg and the man's sperm join up, fertilisation and conception can occur and the story may continue!

151

Activity 2

Making a baby

Look at the eleven sentences below on how a baby is conceived and put them in the correct order by numbering them from 1 to 11, with 1 being the first point in the process.

Sperm swims through the vagina and the uterus (womb) into the fallopian tube.

A couple who are committed to one another decide to have a baby.

The fertilised egg becomes embedded in the wall of the uterus.

The man places his erect penis in the woman's vagina.

One sperm fuses with an egg (fertilisation). This is the moment of conception.

The baby is born.

Sperm leave the penis and enter the vagina (ejaculation).

A sperm cell meets an egg in the fallopian tube. (if ovulation has taken place and an egg has been released from the ovary).

During the next nine months, the fertilised egg develops into a baby.

The fertilised egg travels back through the fallopian tube to the uterus.

The woman notices that she has missed a period and doesn't menstruate.

Think about how well you remembered what you learned in first year and give yourself a rating between 1 and 5. Give yourself 1 if you remembered very little and 5 if you remembered a lot. It is important that you know how your body works. If you gave yourself a low number then identify the gaps in your knowledge and work out what you can do to fill them.

The number I gave myself is _____ because _____

_____

_____

To ensure that I'm familiar with the reproductive systems I can _____

_____

_____

Stages of pregnancy

PowerPoint

Pregnancy is divided into three stages called trimesters.

- First trimester – from conception to week 12

- Second trimester – weeks 13 to 27

- Third trimester – begins in week 28 and continues to birth.

1	2	3	4	5	6	7	8	9
1 Trimester			2 Trimester			3 Trimester		Birth

What happens during each trimester?

First trimester – Weeks 1–12

- The fertilised egg becomes embedded in the wall of the womb about seven days after fertilisation

- First, the brain, the nervous system and the blood circulatory system develop

- At 3 weeks – the heart is beating, and eyes, mouth and ears begin to form

- At 4 weeks – arm and leg buds begin to form

- At 5 weeks – the sex of the baby develops

- At 8 weeks – the baby is eight or ten centimetres

- At 12 weeks – the baby is fully formed and is called a foetus.

> **KEY WORDS**
>
> **Foetus**
> Embryo stage from eight weeks after conception until birth.

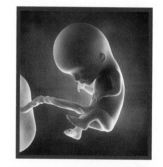

> **KEY WORDS**
>
> **Placenta**
> Organ joining mother and foetus, transferring oxygen and nutrients from mother to baby.

Second trimester – Weeks 13–24

- The placenta is fully formed, allowing oxygen and food to pass from the mother's blood to the baby, through the umbilical cord

- All the baby's organs are fully formed but need time to develop and mature

- The baby begins to move its arms and legs, fingernails form, hair begins to grow and the baby's eyes develop

- At 20 weeks – the mother feels the baby's movements

- At 24 weeks – the baby can hear the mother's heartbeat and voice.

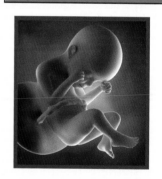

Third trimester – Weeks 25–36

- The baby continues to grow and develop, increasing in size and length.

- The baby spends time sleeping and is wakeful at other times. Organs such as the lungs mature so the baby can breathe independently when it is born.

- The baby moves into a head-down position, ready for birth, and is usually born after 40 weeks

Birth

Scientists are still not quite sure how the process of birth actually begins! We do know there are three stages involved:

Stage 1: This can last for up to 12 hours and sometimes longer

- The muscles of the womb begin to contract, resulting in the start of labour (birth)
- The baby is pushed down towards the opening (cervix) at the base of the womb
- The sac in which the baby has grown and developed over the last nine months (40 weeks) breaks, if it hasn't done so already, and the amniotic fluid flows away (waters breaking)
- The neck of the womb gradually opens.

Stage 2: This can last from 20 minutes to an hour

- The neck of the womb opens (dilates) enough for the mother to push the baby through the birth canal
- The end of this stage is marked by the birth of the baby
- The umbilical cord, the baby's lifeline, is clamped and cut
- The baby cries and takes its first breath, filling its lungs with air.

Stage 3: This can last between five minutes and an hour

- Even though the baby is born the contractions continue until the placenta is pushed out.

The journey of the last nine months has ended with the birth of the baby!

Healthy Mother, Healthy Baby

A mother's health is essential to the good health of her baby. Women who decide to have a baby need to make sure they are in good health before they become pregnant, during the pregnancy and afterwards as well. Women who lead a healthy lifestyle, eat well and exercise regularly, as well as having good medical care when they are pregnant, are less likely to have complications while pregnant and are more likely to give birth to a healthy baby.

Some tips for a healthy pregnancy!

- Plan ahead!
- Before becoming pregnant take folic acid supplements as this reduces the risk of your baby having spina bifida.
- Link in with your local health centre to arrange antenatal/prenatal care (care before your baby's birth).
- Eat a healthy, balanced diet with plenty of protein.
- Avoid food such as raw eggs, mould-ripened cheeses, foods made with unpasteurised milk and under-cooked meat and fish, especially shellfish. These may contain organisms, bacteria or moulds, which could result in food poisoning or miscarriage (loss of the embryo before the twentieth week of pregnancy).
- Avoid alcohol as it passes into the baby across the placenta and can cause Foetal Alcohol Syndrome. This could result in the baby having learning difficulties.
- Never use illegal drugs, as they can cause serious damage to the unborn baby.
- Don't smoke as this increases the risk of miscarriage or of having a stillborn baby (a baby born dead after 24 weeks of pregnancy) or of having a baby with a low birth weight.
- Cut back on caffeine to ensure your baby is a healthy weight.
- Check with your doctor before taking any medication, even over-the-counter painkillers.
- Take plenty of exercise, at least 60 minutes each day.
- Look after your mental health and talk to your doctor if you are feeling depressed or down.
- When you feel tired remember to take some time to rest.

Did You Know?

In 2017, the Irish Medical Organisation estimated that 600 babies are born with Foetal Alcohol Syndrome (FAS) in Ireland each year.

Assessment – Check your learning

Becoming a parent brings huge responsibilities. Just because your body is physically mature enough for parenthood does not mean that you are ready emotionally (how you feel) or psychologically (in your mind). If you are looking after a baby, there are a whole range of practical responsibilities you will have to meet and different demands will be made on you.

With another student, discuss these responsibilities and the ways in which your life would change if you have a baby before you are ready, for example while you are still in school. Write down three ways in which you are not yet ready for parenthood and why it is better for you to wait until you are older.

_____
_____
_____
_____

Sexuality and Sexual Orientation

You will remember that you explored this topic briefly in first year. Let's look at it in more detail now.

KEY WORDS

Sexual orientation
Term used to describe what gender a person is romantically or sexually attracted to.

Activity 3

Danny – a year later

 Animation

You discussed 'Danny's dilemma' on page 139, where he was having a problem with his friends, as he did not want to start going out with anyone. Danny is now in third year and a lot has happened in the past year!

Danny has got on well in school but he is still finding the pressure to be in a relationship difficult to deal with for all sorts of reasons. In the last year Danny has realised he is gay and has come out to his family. They are all on his side and understand and support him. A huge burden has been lifted from Danny's shoulders, now that he has talked to his family, and he feels free to be himself. He is more confident and plans to tell his close friends. However, Danny is still a bit worried about what other people might think. He has recently joined a local club and enjoys going there, especially as he has become friendly with Ged. Ged has come out to his family and friends but isn't in a relationship. He seems very self-confident. Ged and Danny discover that they have loads of interests in common and start spending more and more time together.

KEY WORDS

Inclusive school
A school where lesbian, gay, bisexual and transgender young people, along with people of different identities, are valued and feel safe.

Two months later Danny and Ged begin going out together. Ged is a year ahead of Danny in the same school so they meet up with other friends at lunch and, like everyone else, make plans for the weekend.

1 Think about what it's like to be Danny in your school and about your own attitudes and the values that guide your behaviour. Then look at the statements below and tick if you agree, disagree or are unsure, after each one.

Statements	Agree	Disagree	Unsure
	Green	Red	Orange
1 If other students made jokes about someone being gay I'd laugh to fit in.			
2 If other students made comments about being gay I'd challenge them.			
3 If other students made comments about being gay I'd just say nothing and walk away.			
4 I've often heard someone saying, 'That's so gay' to describe something – an object, clothing or what someone says or does.			
5 It's OK to use the expression 'That's so gay' as long as it's not directed at someone who is gay.			
6 I've never thought about how Danny or other LGBT students might be affected by statements like 'That's so gay'.			
7 I'd be happy for Danny to be my friend in our school.			
8 In our school there are adults who Danny would find easy to talk to if he felt he needed help or support.			
9 A visitor to our school would easily see that it is an inclusive place where LGBT (lesbian, gay, bisexual and transgender) students are respected and valued.			
10 Danny would feel comfortable and safe being open about being gay in our school.			

2 Have a class discussion about these ten statements, using the 'Traffic Lights' pages at the end of your textbook. When your teacher calls out each statement, hold up the relevant page to show whether you agree (green), disagree (red) or are unsure (orange) and discuss your reasons.

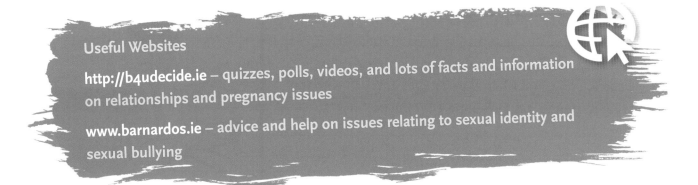

Useful Websites

http://b4udecide.ie – quizzes, polls, videos, and lots of facts and information on relationships and pregnancy issues

www.barnardos.ie – advice and help on issues relating to sexual identity and sexual bullying

In Activity 3 I was surprised by

The statement I found easiest to make a decision about was number ___ because

The statement I found most difficult to make a decision on was number ___ because

Something I learned about myself from Activity 3 is

Something I learned about what it's like to be gay in our school is

Our school is an inclusive school and welcomes young people who are LGBT. We know this because

Assessment – Check your learning

Research an organisation which offers support to young people who are LGBT. Write a column for your school magazine or student newsletter. Include the following:

1 Name of the organisation.

2 Why you might encourage someone to join the organisation.

3 Describe the support the organisation offers to a young LGBT person.

4 Describe how and when they can get in touch with the organisation to get the support they need.

5   Keep your magazine article in your SPHE folder or e-folder and write a summary of the main points from your article below:

_____

_____

_____

_____

_____

_____

Review of Unit 3: *Sexuality, Gender Identity and Sexual Health*

1 In this unit I learned about _____

_____

_____

2 I think that this will help me when _____

_____

_____

3 In this unit I liked _____

_____

_____

4 In this unit I did not like _____

_____

_____

5 I would like to find out more about _____

_____

_____

6 This unit links with (name another unit in SPHE or another subject) _____

_____

_____

UNIT 4 Media Influences on Relationships and Sexuality

KEY WORDS

Media

Media messages

Influence

Learning Outcomes:

This unit helps you to:

1. Increase your awareness of the different kinds of media you encounter every day

2. Describe some of the media messages you receive

3. Explain some of the influences media messages may have on young people your age.

(Tick these off as you complete them.)

The Media and Your Life

As you go about your daily business of relaxing at home, going to school, playing sports, hanging out with friends and so on, you are exposed to many forms of media, media messages and influences, some of which you are not even aware of. Let's explore the idea of media in more detail.

The word media is the plural of the word medium. **Media** includes the different ways through which messages and information are communicated to us. It is important to identify some of the more common kinds of media that you encounter in everyday life, such as newspapers, magazines, TV, radio, the Internet, mobile phones, Twitter, social media websites, billboards, fliers and so on.

KEY WORDS

Media
Any means of communication and how people connect with one another.

You are probably familiar with advertising suggesting how you should look or behave in a particular way, including what hairstyle you should have, what clothes or shoes to wear, what TV programmes to watch and so on. Other media influences include messages to do with your gender or sexuality, and the roles you should play or the way you should behave because of your sex. For example, often men and boys are depicted as being strong and tough, whereas girls and women are depicted as being more passive and weak.

KEY WORDS

Media messages
Information such as words, pictures, signs or symbols conveyed through any form of media

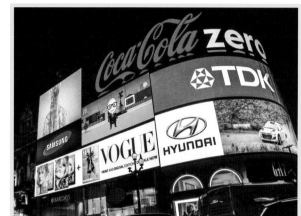

Activity

1

Your daily media

Working in pairs, come up with a list of all the different kinds of media you might encounter in your daily life. Write these on the wall on the right, using a graffiti style. Remember to include what you *read, see* and *hear*, at home, at school and when you are out and about with your friends. Use signs, symbols, drawings or words.

Did You Know?

Graffiti and street art can be a medium through which people express opinions, often about politics or community issues. The word graffiti comes from the Greek word 'graphein' which means 'to write'. Graffiti was first found in ancient Roman architecture but there was no spray paint then! Instead, messages were scratched onto walls.

Activity 2

Media messages are all around us!

Think about what the different forms of media are aiming to do – what messages are they sending you? For example, an advertisement on a billboard may be trying to get you to buy a particular product. Select three forms of media, one for seeing/reading, one for listening and one for watching, and answer the questions below for each form.

1. Name the type of media.

2. Briefly describe what it aims to do.

3. Say whether the message is positive or negative and why you think this is so.

4. Describe how being more aware of the range of media messages and influences you are bombarded with each day might change the way you think.

Medium A: Seeing/reading _____

_____
_____
_____
_____

Medium B: Listening _____

_____
_____
_____
_____

Medium C: Watching _____

_____
_____
_____
_____

LEARNING LOG

A media message I hadn't noticed before is
_____
_____

Now that I am aware of it, in future I will
_____
_____

Media Influences

KEY WORDS

Influence
The power to bring about a change in someone or something without directly forcing them.

Whether you are aware of it or not, media influences can and do shape your behaviour. These influences can be direct, for example advertising campaigns focused on teenagers encouraging you to buy and wear the latest fashions or a specific label, or advertisements showing that it is 'cool' to be seen smoking or drinking. Influences can also be indirect – where you are not aware that you are being influenced. For example, the use of aggressive language in video games and in the lyrics of songs can normalise this language, making it seem like this is ordinary behaviour and language, whereas in fact it is degrading and insulting.

Not all media influences are negative. For example, many young people use different types of media to develop an awareness about society and the wider world, inspiring them to decide how they want to live their life, and helping them to form their own values and attitudes. Using social media can also help young people to develop social skills and make new friendships, as long as they are aware of the need to stay safe online. Use of blogs and other social media can also improve literacy skills.

Media literacy

You are now more aware of the range of media influences and messages you are overloaded with each day. Being aware of these influences is the first step in being able to manage them.

Let's explore this further and think about some of the media messages that may influence young people.

Activity

3

How are you influenced?

Think about the different kinds of media you listed in Activity 1, such as magazines, reality TV programmes, billboards, social media, the Internet, song lyrics and so on. In groups of four, discuss the different types of messages that the media give to and say about young people and how they try to influence you. Write two examples under each type of message on the Post-its.

Messages about your gender, (being male or female) and gender roles (including stereotypes):

Messages about how you should behave:

Messages about anger/violence:

Messages about good feelings:

Messages about sex and sexuality:

Have a class discussion, with feedback from all the groups, and see what you have in common with the other groups' findings. Then, using the pointers to guide you, complete the assessment below and keep it in your e-folder or SPHE folder.

Assessment – Check your learning

Write an article for a magazine or blog aimed at young people. The title of the article is 'Under the influence!' Use the questions below to help get you started.

1. In what way might different media messages influence how young people look, think and behave?

2. How might these messages influence how young people view their friendships and relationships?

3. How do you think a young person might feel if they weren't able to live up to the expectations placed on them by the media?

4. What pressures might these messages place on young people?

5. What might help them to deal with these pressures?

6. How would you like to see young people represented in a more positive way in the media?

7. What skills have you learned in SPHE that will help you to deal with these messages and influences?

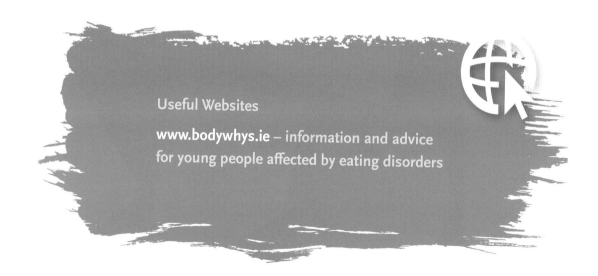

Useful Websites

www.bodywhys.ie – information and advice for young people affected by eating disorders

Review of Unit 4: *Media Influences on Relationships and Sexuality*

1 In this unit I learned about _____

_____

_____

2 I think that this will help me when _____

_____

_____

3 In this unit I liked _____

_____

_____

4 In this unit I did not like _____

_____

_____

5 I would like to find out more about _____

_____

_____

6 This unit links with (name another unit in SPHE or another subject) _____

_____

_____

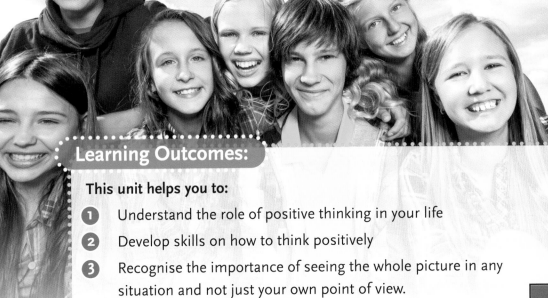

UNIT **1** Positive Mental Health

Learning Outcomes:

This unit helps you to:

1 Understand the role of positive thinking in your life ○

2 Develop skills on how to think positively ○

3 Recognise the importance of seeing the whole picture in any situation and not just your own point of view. ○

(Tick off as you complete them.)

KEY WORDS

Reframe

Perception

It's How You Look at It

In *Health and Wellbeing: SPHE 1* you looked briefly at the link between thoughts, feelings and behaviour.

Your thoughts have a powerful effect on how you feel about something and what you can do in a situation. For example, negative thoughts can become a vicious cycle, but if you can change how you think about something, this has a knock-on effect on how you feel and on how you behave.

THOUGHTS

BEHAVIOUR

FEELINGS

KEY WORDS

Reframe
Changing the way you see things, saying 'Let's look at this another way' so that you see something differently.

If you take a minute, slow down and do not jump to conclusions, then you can think positively, reframe the situation and the outcome will be much better for everyone.

 PowerPoint

Here is an example:

Situation		You had a bad morning at school and at lunchtime you see two of your friends in the canteen. You give them a wave and head over to sit with them. Before you reach them, they start laughing, get their bags and head off to their lockers.	
		**UNHELPFUL**	**HELPFUL**
Thoughts		They blanked me. They don't want me to sit with them.	They mustn't have seen me. I'll catch up with them later.
Feelings	**Emotional**	Sad, angry, rejected	Curiosity
	Physical	Anxiety, stomach upset	No change
Behaviour/Actions		Avoid them, be snappy or moody with them	Ask them where they were off to

Activity 1

Reframing

Using the example above as a guide, read the situation below, reframe it and write in your answers.

Situation		You ask your mum if you can get an Xbox or a PlayStation for Christmas. She says no.	
		UNHELPFUL	**HELPFUL**
Thoughts			
Feelings	**Emotional**		
	Physical		
Behaviour/Actions			

Remember

Your mind is a powerful thing – it can change the way you see things, the way you feel and the way you act and react.

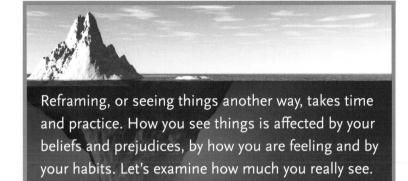

Reframing, or seeing things another way, takes time and practice. How you see things is affected by your beliefs and prejudices, by how you are feeling and by your habits. Let's examine how much you really see.

Activity 2

Seeing the full picture

Look at these two famous images. Under each one write down what you first saw when you looked at it.

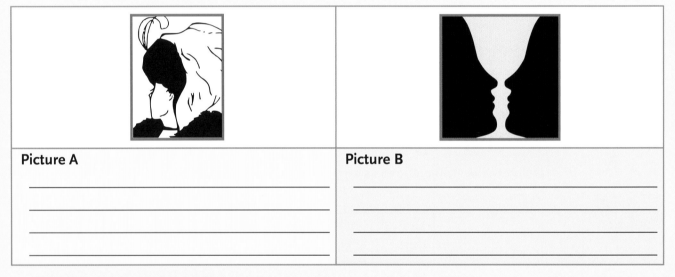

Picture A

_____

_____

_____

_____

Picture B

_____

_____

_____

_____

1. In picture A can you see both the old woman's face in profile and the young woman looking away from you?

2. In picture B can you see both the vase and the black silhouette of two faces looking at each other?

3. What surprised you about these pictures or film clips?

_____

_____

_____

_____

For more examples of changing your first perceptions, your teacher will provide you with some short film clips.

4. What have you learned from this exercise?

_____

_____

_____

_____

Your sense of perception

How you perceive something (what you think is the case) isn't always the way it is and there is usually another way of looking at it. For example, if you arrive into class without your homework you are much more likely to think the teacher is staring at you than if you have ia clear conscience.

Things are not always what they seem and your beliefs can change what you see or the way that you perceive something. It is important to never make assumptions – to keep an open mind and check things out fully. For example, if somebody tells you that Jo, the new student in second year, is trouble and you assume this is true, then you might meet Jo with that prejudice in mind and you may fit what Jo does and says into that stereotype. Instead, you should keep an open mind and wait until you have talked to Jo a few times yourself before deciding what he/she is like.

Minds are like parachutes. They work better when they are open!

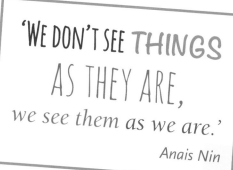

'WE DON'T SEE THINGS AS THEY ARE, we see them as we are.'

Anais Nin

Assessment – Check your learning

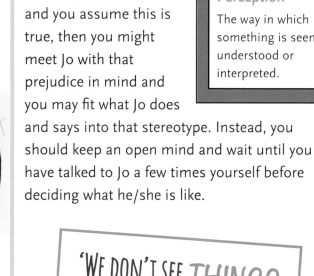

Using the Internet, find two more pictures that are examples of something where you do not see the full picture and where your first perception of what you see is not accurate. Make a class display of all the students' pictures and come up with a creative name for it. The pictures can be saved in either your SPHE folder or your e-folder.

Staying Positive

Sometimes it can be really hard to be positive, think positive thoughts and see the upside of things. Ten steps you can take to help you are listed in the box below. These steps won't work all the time, but looking at things positively will become a habit if you make an effort to keep practising doing it.

Avoid negative people – keep them away!

Don't let yourself get overtired and 'ratty'.

Eat well, exercise and get enough sleep.

Don't sweat the small stuff. Ask yourself if it really matters. Is it so important? Will I remember this next month?

Do positive things for others – it makes **you** feel more positive.

Practise deep breathing, relaxation and mindfulness. (See *Health and Wellbeing: SPHE 1*)

Smile – it's that simple.

Don't be too hard on yourself. Tell yourself that you're doing the best you can today and that you will probably be able to do better tomorrow.

Remind yourself of all of the things you are grateful for. This is important.

Never compare yourself with others. You do not know what is going on in their lives.

½ air

½ water

TECHNICALLY THE GLASS IS ALWAYS FULL

My best tip to help me stay positive is

LEARNING LOG

Useful Websites

www.yourmentalhealth.ie – ideas and tips on things you can do to feel well

www.samaritans.org – offers a 24-hour service if you feel you need a good chat

Activity 3

Positive power

Make a list of all the things people in your class do to keep themselves positive. Choose one to try out during the week and write a summary of what happened.

_____
_____
_____
_____
_____
_____
_____

Review of Unit 1: _Positive Mental Health_

1. In this unit I learned about _____
_____
_____

2. I think that this will help me when _____
_____
_____

3. In this unit I liked _____
_____
_____

4. In this unit I did not like _____
_____
_____

5. I would like to find out more about _____
_____
_____

6. This unit links with (name another unit in SPHE or another subject) _____
_____
_____

STRAND **4** My Mental Health

UNIT **2** Mental Health and Mental Ill-Health

KEY WORDS

Mental health

Stigma

Counselling therapies

Learning Outcomes:

This unit helps you to:

1 Explore your, and other people's, attitudes to mental health ○

2 Understand the close link between physical and mental health ○

3 Discuss mental health issues experienced by young people ○

4 Find common sources of help for mental health problems. ○

(Tick off as you complete them.)

Exploring Mental Health

In *Health and Wellbeing: SPHE 1* you were introduced to the idea of being mentally healthy and that it was just as important as being physically healthy. This year we are going to look at this topic in more detail.

The World Health Organization (WHO) defines mental health as:

'A state of wellbeing in which every individual:

● Can recognise his or her own potential

● Can cope with the normal stresses of life

● Can work productively and fruitfully

● Is able to make a contribution to his or her community.'

As you can see, mental health is about having good self-esteem, being involved in doing meaningful things and being able to get through difficult times.

MENS SANA IN CORPORE SANO

This famous Latin quotation is translated as: 'A healthy mind in a healthy body'. The connection between physical and mental health is very strong. If you are physically sick, with a bad cold for example, you will have obvious physical symptoms, such as sneezing, a high temperature and a headache.

But having a bad cold also affects your mental health. You will probably be in a bad mood, find it hard to concentrate and have no enthusiasm for doing the things that usually interest you. Likewise, if you are experiencing a mental health issue, for example severe stress, you might have physical symptoms such as a rash, a headache or feeling extremely tired.

Physical health and mental health go hand in hand.

Activity

1

Assigning the signs

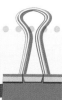

List of Symptoms

Below are some common symptoms of both physical and mental illnesses. Working in pairs, decide if each symptom belongs in the physical or mental health box and write it into its correct category. Then answer the questions on page 174.

Chest pain

Tiredness

Eczema

Sweating

Headache

Poor concentration

Upset stomach

Loss of appetite

Insomnia

Joint pains

Aching limbs

Crying

Diarrhoea

Dizziness

Confusion

 Physical health

 Mental health

1 List any symptoms that could be associated with both physical and mental illness.

_____

_____

2 What did you learn from this activity?

_____

_____

Attitudes to mental health

In *Health and Wellbeing: SPHE 1* you learned about positive mental health and how to deal with your feelings and cope with tough times. You looked at knowing where to get help and how to take care of your mental wellbeing by using breathing exercises, relaxation and mindfulness. Like physical health, if you do not look after your mental health, you risk getting mental health problems.

In this unit, you will learn about the common mental health issues that affect young people, their friends and families. To start with let's see how you feel about mental health issues.

Warning!

It is really important that you remember your SPHE 'Class Ground Rules' and:

- Do not say anything that could hurt others
- Do not share personal, private information
- Respect confidentiality.

2 How do you feel?

1 On your own, read the eight statements below and tick whether you agree, disagree or are unsure, after each one.

Statements	Agree	Disagree	Unsure
	Green	Red	Orange
1 If I had mental health problems I wouldn't want people knowing about them.			
2 Only certain types of people can become mentally ill.			
3 If I had a mental health problem I would know what to do about it.			
4 About one in ten people will have mental health issues in their lifetime.			
5 I don't know much about mental health issues.			
6 Women are more likely to get help if they have mental health problems.			
7 It is easy to tell if someone has a mental health issue.			
8 The best way to treat mental health issues is with medication.			

2 Have a class discussion about these eight statements, using the 'Traffic Lights' pages at the end of your textbook. When your teacher calls out each statement, hold up the relevant page to show whether you agree (green), disagree (red) or are unsure (orange) and discuss your reasons.

The stigma of mental health problems

According to Mental Health Ireland, people with mental health problems say that the social stigma attached to these issues and the discrimination they experience can make their difficulties worse and make it harder to recover. This can affect their chances of getting work, a permanent home or being in a steady, long-term relationship (see www.mentalhealthireland.ie). Learning the facts and talking about mental health issues are important ways of fighting this stigma.

Did You Know?

In Australia, three out of four people with a mental illness report that they have experienced stigma and feel that they are labelled by their illness. *(www.health.wa.gov.au)*

KEY WORDS

Stigma

A mark of shame or disgrace causing people to be treated differently. The word originally came from a mark burned onto slaves to single them out.

One thing about mental health problems that I didn't know before today is

LEARNING LOG

Common mental health issues for young people

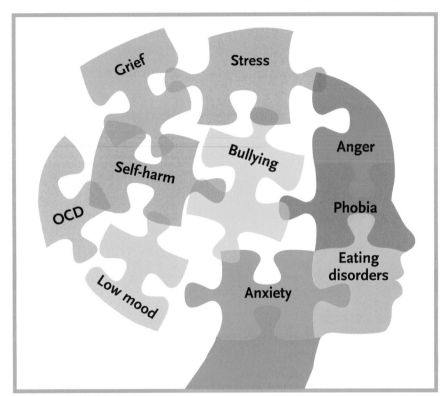

Most young people know a lot about common physical illnesses and can easily tell the difference between a sore throat, measles, toothache and so on. But when it comes to common mental health problems your knowledge may be a bit fuzzier. This can result in young people being unwilling to engage with a friend or someone else they know who has mental health problems and then this can increase the levels of stigma the person feels.

Did You Know?

'While people can experience mental ill-health at any time of their life, international evidence shows that the onset [start] of mental disorders peaks during adolescent and early adult years. . . . by the age of 13, one in three young people in Ireland is likely to have experienced some type of mental disorder.'

(The Mental Health of Young People in Ireland, Royal College of Surgeons Ireland)

Activity 3

Knowing the difference

 PowerPoint

You may know more about mental health problems than you realise. Read the six descriptions of common mental health issues for young people and see if you can match them with one of these terms:

Claustrophobia   **Obsessive Compulsive Disorder (OCD)**   **Low mood**

Anorexia   **Anger issues**   **Anxiety**

When you have finished, your teacher will show you a slide show with more information on these mental health issues.

Case 1

I find it so hard to manage my weight that I often weigh my food or rigidly count the calories even in a single piece of fruit. When I am with friends I often pretend that I have already eaten so I don't have to eat. My friends tell me that I'm too thin but when I look in the mirror I am upset by how fat I am. I need to lose about three pounds to reach my target weight of seven stone.

_____

Case 2

I am often very tired and have no interest in going out with my friends. Other times I feel OK. I find it hard to sleep and tend to worry a lot. A lot of the time I get overcome with a feeling of sadness and think I am not interesting to anyone.

_____

Case 3

I am constantly worried about cleanliness. I won't use a cup or plate without washing it first – even if it looks clean. I never share water bottles or drink out of something someone else has touched. When I go to bed I have to be certain sure the pillow is clean. I can't sleep on a pillow or use a towel that has been used by someone else.

_____

Case 4

When something bugs me I lash out: swearing, shouting, sometimes breaking furniture or even punching people. I can get very aggressive and call people who annoy me names, threaten them and frighten them. I just can't stop myself and I get so worked up that my fists clench, I can feel my face going red and my heart starts pounding.

_____

Case 5

I can't go into tight spaces. The attic, for example. Or down a narrow tunnel. Once on a school tour, we visited caves and a little way in I just lost it – started sweating and panicking and had to be taken out and the teacher stayed in the restaurant with me. It has now gotten so bad that I can't even wear a jumper if the neck is tight as I freak out pulling it on over my head. Sometimes I wake up in an awful state because in my dream I have something over my face and I can't breathe.

_____

Case 6

I worry constantly and about every little thing. I feel overwhelmed by things and situations that I used to be able to manage and find myself on the brink of tears. I find it hard to sleep and have difficulty concentrating and am so irritable if things get on top of me.

_____

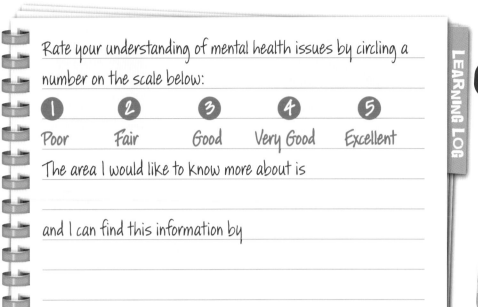

Rate your understanding of mental health issues by circling a number on the scale below:

① Poor   **②** Fair   **③** Good   **④** Very Good   **⑤** Excellent

The area I would like to know more about is

and I can find this information by

Did You Know?

More than 50 per cent of young people in Ireland will meet the criteria for a mental health illness before they reach age 25, a study by the Royal College of Surgeons Ireland (RCSI) and the Mater Hospital has found.

You are not alone – getting help

Most common mental health problems, like most physical health problems, are temporary and can be treated easily with the appropriate help. But, even though one in three young people aged 11–13 will experience a mental health problem, the stigma of mental health can often stop people getting help. However, help is available and it is really important to get it so that you can move on with your life.

Getting help:

- Prevention is better than cure! Re-read the 'Five a day for mental wellbeing' section in *Health and Wellbeing: SPHE 1* (pages 172–173)
- Talk about your problems before they even become problems. Get into the habit of tuning into how you feel and discussing it with someone you trust
- Talk to friends and family if you think you have a concern
- Talk to your school counsellor
- Get some advice from the mental health agencies in Ireland (see the list of useful websites on page 179)
- Ask your parent/guardian to bring you to your doctor.

You may find that counselling therapies or medication, or both, will help you.

KEY WORDS

Counselling therapies
Working with a trained counsellor or psychotherapist to resolve mental health issues.

Assessment – Check your learning

In groups of three, using the websites below and what you have learned in this unit, research one of the common mental health issues experienced by young people and present the information to your class by using one of these methods:

- Give a talk to your class
- Show a PowerPoint presentation
- Make a poster.

Demi Lovato founded Be Vocal: Speak Up for Mental Health to encourage people to share their stories of mental illness.

Useful Websites

www.yourmentalhealth.ie – has an online wellbeing workshop and county-by-county supports, with 'Common problems' dealt with in the 'Mind yourself and others' section

www.mentalhealthireland.ie – the 'Help and Information' section has a great A to Z with all the information you need

www.aware.ie – information and help for people with depression and bipolar, with advice for teens and relatives as well

www.samaritans.ie – provides a listening service for anyone in distress

www.bodywhys.ie – excellent information and support for people affected by all types of eating disorders

www.pieta.ie – information on suicide, suicidal thoughts and self-harming

Review of Unit 2: *Mental Health and Mental Ill-Health*

1 In this unit I learned about _____
_____
_____

2 I think that this will help me when _____
_____
_____

3 In this unit I liked _____
_____
_____

4 In this unit I did not like _____
_____
_____

5 I would like to find out more about _____
_____
_____

6 This unit links with (name another unit in SPHE or another subject) _____
_____
_____

UNIT 3 Dealing with Tough Times

Learning Outcomes:

This unit helps you to:

① Understand how resilience can help you handle life's challenges ◯

② Develop simple ways of building up your resilience ◯

(Tick off as you complete them.)

Resilience

In *Health and Wellbeing: SPHE 1* you learned that **resilience** means being able to manage the ups and downs of life and bounce back after experiencing difficulties.

Resilience can:

- Increase your confidence so that you try new things
- Make it easier for you to get over difficulties in your life, such as having a fight with a friend, losing a match or not making the team in the first place
- Help you to cope with more serious upsets, such as your parents separating or a relative dying
- Help your school performance.

You can build up your resilience so that you are better at dealing with the difficulties in your life.

KEY WORDS

Endorphins

Resilience

The five Bs of building resilience

Bee Active

Physically unwinding helps you to unwind mentally – it's a stress buster so having hobbies, doing sports or any type of regular exercise will increase your resilience. It's even better if they involve other people. Having a passion for something is really important in building your resilience.

Bee Friend

Having a good friend or friends and people who are close to you is the kind of support that has a very powerful effect on your wellbeing.

Bee Lief

Having a belief system or a sense of meaning in your life, a goal and a set of beliefs helps you to make sense of life and get through tough times.

Bee Long

Having a sense of roots, of place and of belonging, by being part of a family, clubs, your local community, makes you feel you are part of something and the support you get from this helps to give you strength if you are feeling low or lost.

Just Bee

Taking time to relax and recharge your batteries and not letting yourself get worn out or run down, eating healthily, sleeping well, exercising, doing meditation, mindfulness, yoga or relaxation techniques (see *Health and Wellbeing: SPHE 1*) will all help to build your resilience.

Activity 1

My well of resilience

It is important to remember that you can work on building up your resilience by putting time into the five areas highlighted on the buckets above. Think of resilience as a well. You fill the well when you can so that when you really need to be resilient there is a reservoir built up.

In the space on each of the buckets above write in what you do in your life to build your resilience levels in that area. Then answer the questions below.

1 Which bucket do you use the most to fill up your resilience?

_____

2 Which one do you need to work on?

_____

One area where I find it difficult to build up my resilience is _____

This is because _____

_____

_____

LEARNING LOG

Endorphins – nature's high

Endorphins are known as the body's 'feel-good' chemicals. Their release into the body triggers feelings of pleasure, wellbeing and pain relief. They also protect you against depression, relieve stress and anxiety, and improve your mood.

The most common way of releasing endorphins into your blood is exercise. You have probably heard of a 'runner's high', which is the feeling of extreme happiness you can get from fast running or vigorous exercise. Another way of increasing endorphins in your body is to have a good belly laugh.

KEY WORDS

Endorphins

'Feel-good' chemicals released in the brain that can cause a feeling of euphoria or elation and reduce feelings of pain. Physical exercise can cause the release of endorphins.

Did You Know?

If you are feeling upset, one thing that will help you bounce back is laughter. Laughter boosts your immune system and helps fight infection, lower stress levels and release endorphins. It is a terrific anger-buster! Laughter also helps people to bond and build connections, and helps your blood vessels to function better because you take in so much oxygen when you are laughing. This can help to protect you against heart attacks.

Activity 2

It's no joke!

Working in pairs, come up with a joke that one of you then tells the class. It can be corny, like the Christmas cracker jokes, but it must not be racist, sexist or offensive. What's important is that it makes people laugh! Here are a few to get you going!

There were two ducks from Northern Ireland. One said, 'Quack! Quack!'

The other said: I'm going as quack as I can!

What would you call a man lying outside the door? Matt.

What would you call a man with a shovel? Doug.

Why did the calf cross the road? To get to the 'udder' side!

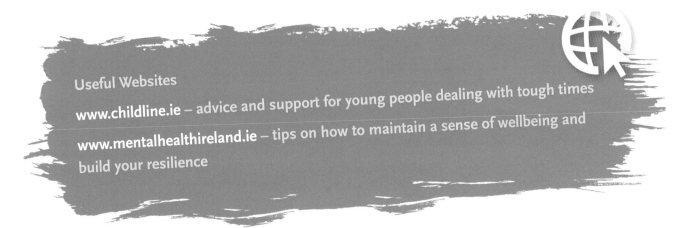

Useful Websites

www.childline.ie – advice and support for young people dealing with tough times

www.mentalhealthireland.ie – tips on how to maintain a sense of wellbeing and build your resilience

Review of Unit 3: *Dealing with Tough Times*

1 In this unit I learned about _____

_____

_____

2 I think that this will help me when _____

_____

_____

3 In this unit I liked _____

_____

_____

4 In this unit I did not like _____

_____

_____

5 I would like to find out more about _____

_____

_____

6 This unit links with (name another unit in SPHE or another subject) _____

_____

_____

My Mental Health

Loss and Bereavement

Learning Outcomes:

This unit helps you to:

1. Understand that change and loss are a normal part of life ⬡
2. Become aware of the five stages in the journey through grief ⬡
3. Learn about the physical, emotional, social and spiritual effects of loss and bereavement ⬡
4. Explore how someone who is grieving can be helped and can get help. ⬡

(Tick off as you complete them.)

Loss in Your Life

Last year you looked at how your life changes as you get older. All of these changes, even the ones you look forward to, often involve a loss. For example, you may be delighted to have moved on to post-primary school but you miss your friends from primary school and having less homework!

KEY WORDS

Change
Grief

Remember

Be aware of your SPHE 'Class Ground Rules' while doing this exercise. Only share what you feel comfortable with other people knowing.

All through your life you will experience different kinds of loss. What might seem a small loss to one person could be very upsetting to someone else. It totally depends on the person. For example, some people get very upset about their pet dying, while another person might just get another one and move on.

The road map of my life

The image of the road represents your life so far, beginning when you were born and ending at the age you are now. The changes that most second-year students have in common are marked in. Write in 'How you felt' and 'How you coped' in each circle.

Mark in the other changes that have happened in your life. Make a new circle beside each change, divide it into three parts like the other circles and fill in the sections. Draw an arrow from the circle to the point on your life-line when it happened. For example, if the change is 'Started primary school', under 'Felt' you could write 'Excited but frightened' and under 'Coped', 'Had a brother in the school'.

Sample changes: a pet dying, moving to a new house, a grandparent passing away, getting a new baby brother or sister, falling out with a friend, giving up a sport or a pastime, making new friends and so on.

If you are not happy for others to find out about a particular change in your life, you can just put an X on the map, at the age you were when it happened. Then answer the questions.

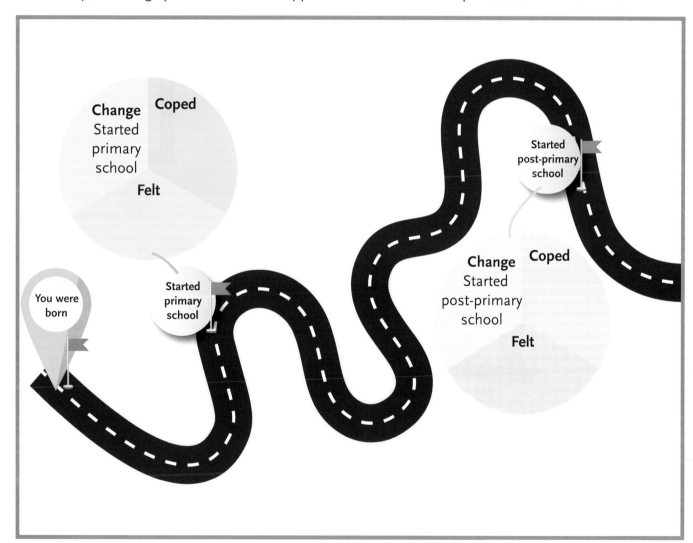

1. Discuss your road map and what you have included with the student beside you.

2. Check if they have similar milestones on their road map and if they coped in the same way as you.

3. On your own, rank the change in your life so far, from the most important to the least important, with one being the most important.

Change, loss and grief

Change is a part of life and, as you learned in *Health and Wellbeing: SPHE 1*, each change can involve a loss and a gain. Experiencing loss can bring out a range of feelings (responses) in people. These feelings can then affect the way you behave. This sense of loss and the feelings that go with it are called grief.

KEY WORDS

Change
To become different; to transform.

Loss and grief – different for everyone

When you suffer a loss it is upsetting and it can be difficult to work your way through it. As no two people are the same, no two people experience loss in the same way. Even if someone close to you, for example your brother or sister, is experiencing a similar loss, such as the death of a family member or your parents separating, they will have their own unique response to it as everybody goes through grief differently.

There are five stages to grief – denial, anger, bargaining, depression and acceptance. You may go through them in any order, sometimes experiencing more than one stage at the same time. You may return to a stage at any time, and for any number of times.

KEY WORDS

Grief
The intense mental anguish or sorrow felt as a result of loss.

The five stages of grief

PowerPoint

Did You Know?

If a family member dies or leaves suddenly it's not unusual for you to feel guilty because you had a row or were unkind the last time you saw them. It is normal to feel this way.

LEARNING LOG

Look back at the change that you ranked number 1 in Activity 1. Did you go through any of the five stages of grief as you dealt with this change and loss?

Effects of loss and bereavement

You have already learned that everyone responds differently to loss and grief and that it's very personal. Some factors that affect how you might manage grief are:

- Your relationship with the person you lost – are you feeling guilty about something you said, did or wished for?
- The other things that are going on in your life. If you have happy, secure relationships or are busy, this can help to lessen the impact of a loss
- Whether the loss was sudden or unexpected
- Your culture – in some cultures grief is expressed openly with loud crying and wailing, while other cultures are more reserved and it can be more difficult for people to express their grief

- Whether or not the person was suffering and in pain
- If you have experienced other losses in the past, as these can come back to you at this point
- Your support network – some people may have close friends or family who will talk openly about the loss and what they are feeling
- Your age – younger children may not fully realise that the person is not coming back.

Activity 2

Physical and emotional effects

Working in pairs, find the seventeen words related to the effects of loss and bereavement in the wordsearch below. Some of these are physical effects and others are emotional. Use two different coloured pens/pencils to mark the words – one colour for the physical effects and a different colour for the emotional effects. The words can appear in any direction, including backwards!

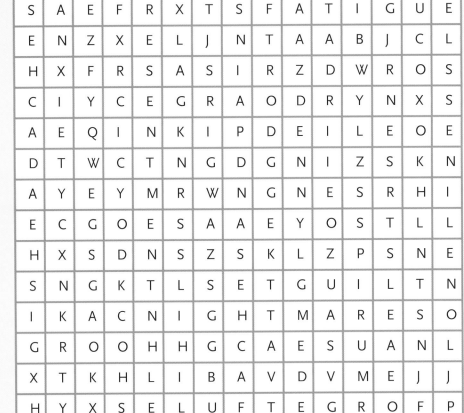

S	A	E	F	R	X	T	S	F	A	T	I	G	U	E
E	N	Z	X	E	L	J	N	T	A	A	B	J	C	L
H	X	F	R	S	A	S	I	R	Z	D	W	R	O	S
C	I	Y	C	E	G	R	A	O	D	R	Y	N	X	S
A	E	Q	I	N	K	I	P	D	E	I	L	E	O	E
D	T	W	C	T	N	G	D	G	N	I	Z	S	K	N
A	Y	E	Y	M	R	W	N	G	N	E	S	R	H	I
E	C	G	O	E	S	A	A	E	Y	O	S	T	L	L
H	X	S	D	N	S	Z	S	K	L	Z	P	S	N	E
S	N	G	K	T	L	S	E	T	G	U	I	L	T	N
I	K	A	C	N	I	G	H	T	M	A	R	E	S	O
G	R	O	O	H	H	G	C	A	E	S	U	A	N	L
X	T	K	H	L	I	B	A	V	D	V	M	E	J	J
H	Y	X	S	E	L	U	F	T	E	G	R	O	F	P
G	Z	D	W	D	K	P	G	D	Q	J	N	N	T	J

Aches and	Anxiety	Fear	Headaches	Nausea	Sadness
pains	Crying	Forgetful	Insomnia	Nightmares	Shock
Anger	Fatigue	Guilt	Loneliness	Resentment	Weight loss

Did You Know?

Anger felt after a loss can often be **projected** onto other targets, for example the doctor, a family member, a teacher or God. The grief-stricken person can be confused about where their anger is coming from, so they blame someone else. This may be particularly true of a young person who has been bereaved.

Bereavement and loss also have social and spiritual effects:

Social effects
- Friends may avoid you because they do not know what to do or say
- You don't want to go out or to see your friends.

Spiritual effects
- You may question the existence of God
- You feel the person you lost is with you and you talk to them a lot.

Parents Separating

Parents separating can be a major change in a young person's life. Sometimes, however, it may be a relief as there might have been tension and fear in the home if your parents were fighting a lot and now that's over.

If your parents are separating you need to let them know how you feel and what's going on with you. For example, 'What are your fears?', 'What do you think is going to happen next?', 'What do you want to happen?' If you need help to sort out what you want to say to your parents, you can discuss it with your school counsellor, a trusted adult or Childline (Tel: 1800 666 666). You could also write to each parent and tell them what you need.

Remember

You are not the cause of your parents splitting up and you can't stop it happening.

Have a look at the Rainbows Ireland website (www.rainbowsireland.ie) as it is an association that helps to support young people whose parents are separating.

Activity 3

Things to remember that might help a friend (or yourself) get through grief

1 It takes as long as it takes – there is no normal.

2 No, you don't know how they are feeling. Everyone's grief is different.

3 Each of the five stages of grief is healthy – and necessary.

4 Focus on the 'now' – remember your mindfulness from *Health and Wellbeing: SPHE 1*.

5 Don't tell them to be strong.

6 Ask them what they need, don't guess. If they say 'nothing' or 'I'm fine', make them tea, give them chocolate or a hug if you're not too embarrassed or tell them a joke.

7 It's OK to be happy.

8 Some people find that writing a journal, planting a tree or talking about the person (constantly) helps.

9 Remember to check in on your friend.

10 Include them in events and trips. They can say no if they don't feel up to it.

11 If you are worried about someone (or yourself) get help from the school counsellor, a trusted adult or check out the websites on the next page.

Read the eleven points above and then answer the questions.

❶ From your experience, write one or two other helpful pieces of advice in the space below.

_____

_____

_____

❷ Do you think any of the eleven points are unhelpful and could make matters worse? Explain your answer.

_____

_____

_____

You can get help here:

- Your school counsellor

- www.rainbowsireland.ie – helps young people who are affected by loss due to death, separation or divorce

- Barnardos bereavement helpline – Tel: 01 4732110 (Monday – Thursday, 10.00 a.m. – 12.00 noon)

- www.bereavementireland.com – a bereavement counselling service with lots of helpful information and a helpline for young people

- Samaritans Ireland – Tel: 116 123 (24 hours a day, 365 days a year) or go to www.samaritans.org or text them at 087 260 9090

- TeenLine Ireland – Freephone: 1800 833 634 or their free text service is open every day of the year (8.00 p.m. – 11.00 p.m.). Text TEEN to 50015. #WeListen

Remember

People who have suffered a loss may forget what you said but they will remember how you made them feel.

LEARNING LOG

I think school is important in helping students to deal with grief because

Assessment – Check your learning

Animation

Mending hearts

Get into groups of four and your teacher will tell you which case study to work on. Read your case study and, using what you have learned so far, make a plan of action to help Leah and Inez or Peter.

Your group must decide who will attend at the case conference, for example the school guidance counsellor, class teacher, parents, other friends, the young people themselves.

Under **Issues** you should be clear about:

- What kind of loss is each person dealing with?

- Are there other problems as well?

Under **Actions**:

- Make suggestions about how they can help each other, and themselves, to deal with this loss

- What role do the people at the case conference have in helping these young people to deal with their issues?

- Are there other people who have a role in helping?

Case Conference

Case 1: Leah and Inez

Leah and Inez have been friends since the first day they started school. They are like sisters and have sat beside each other at school since day one. They spend the weekends and holidays together as well. They have almost finished second year and are looking forward to the summer holidays but in the past few days Leah has noticed that Inez seems miserable.

She won't tell Leah what is bothering her. Today Leah learned that Inez's parents are separating. She has to go and live with her mother in another part of the country. They are both devastated.

Attending

_____

_____

Issues

_____

_____

_____

_____

_____

Actions

_____

_____

_____

_____

_____

_____

Case Conference

Case 2: Peter

Peter and his brother Dan were best friends even though Dan, at 19, was five years older than him. Peter looked up to Dan – he had loads of friends, played soccer with the local club, was a member of a band, had a part-time job in a garage, had bought a motorbike and was training to be a mechanic.

One rainy night when Dan was coming home from band practice, he skidded on gravel and was seriously injured. After two days on life support Dan died.

In the three months since this happened Peter has not been sleeping, he can't concentrate, his work at school has disimproved and he can't be bothered with anything. Yesterday his favourite teacher spoke to him after class about his attitude. Peter walked off, yelling, 'Get off my case!'.

Attending

_____

_____

Issues

_____

_____

_____

_____

Actions

_____

_____

_____

_____

Useful Websites

www.rainbowsireland.ie – helps young people who are affected by loss due to death, separation or divorce

www.barnardos.ie – information on dealing with loss for young people

www.bereavementireland.com – a bereavement counselling service with lots of helpful information and a helpline for young people

Review of Unit 4: *Loss and Bereavement*

1. In this unit I learned about _____

_____

_____

2. I think that this will help me when _____

_____

_____

3. In this unit I liked _____

_____

_____

4. In this unit I did not like _____

_____

_____

5. I would like to find out more about _____

_____

_____

6. This unit links with (name another unit in SPHE or another subject) _____

_____

_____

NOTES

NOTES